Wildlife in Peril

WILDLIFE IN PERIL

THE ENDANGERED

MAMMALS OF

COLORADO

River Otter • Black-Footed Ferret
Wolverine • Lynx
Grizzly Bear • Gray Wolf

JOHN A. MURRAY

foreword by James B. Ruch, Director
Colorado Division of Wildlife

ROBERTS RINEHART, INC. PUBLISHERS

This book is dedicated to its publisher, Rick Rinehart, in grateful acknowledgement of his encouragement, guidance, and support.

Copyright © 1987 by John A. Murray
Published by Roberts Rinehart, Inc. Publishers
Post Office Box 3161   Boulder, Colorado 80303
International Standard Book Numbers 0-911797-27-0 (cloth)
and 0-911797-28-9 (paper)
Library of Congress Catalog Card Number 87-60912
Printed in the United States of America

All royalties from the sale of this book will be donated to the Nongame Fund, Colorado Division of Wildlife.

Contents

It was a great, wild country. In the creek bottoms there were a good many ranches; but we only occasionally passed by these, on our way to our hunting grounds in the wilderness along the edge of the snow-line. The mountains crowded close together in chain, peak, and tableland; all the higher ones were wrapped in an unrent shroud of snow. We saw a good many deer, and fresh sign of elk. . . . The Country was open. The high peaks were bare of trees. Cottonwoods, and occasionally dwarfed birch or maple and willows, fringed the streams; aspens grew in groves higher up. There were pinyons and cedars on the slopes of the foothills; spruce clustered here and there in the cooler ravines and valleys and high up the mountains.

—Theodore Roosevelt (While hunting lion and bear near Glenwood Springs, Colorado) *Outdoor Pastimes of an American Hunter*

Acknowledgements

A book of this scope can only be undertaken with the assistance of a large number of individuals. It could not have been written without the help of the following people and agencies and the resources they made available to me. I am indebted to each of them. While acknowledging the importance of their contributions, all errors of facts are of course my own.

The following individuals reviewed the manuscript as indicated. While there remains disagreement on some questions, the finished book includes many of their suggestions. Without their careful reading, this would have been quite a different work.

David Armstrong, Professor of Natural Science at the University of Colorado at Boulder (entire); Elaine Anderson, Pleistocene mammalogist at the Denver Natural History Museum (paleontology); Tom Beck, wildlife researcher with the Colorado Division of Wildlife (entire); Steve Bissell, biologist with the Colorado Division of Wildlife (entire); Tim Clark, Adjunct Professor of Biology at Idaho State University and President of Biota Research and Consulting, Inc. (black-footed ferret); Kathy Fagerstone, research biologist, Denver Wildlife Research Center, U.S. Department of Agriculture (black-footed ferret); Patsy Goodman, Public Affairs Coordinator, Central Region, Colorado Division of Wildlife (river otter); Jim Halfpenny, Research Associate with the Institute of Arctic and Alpine Research at the University of Colorado at Boulder (lynx and wolverine); Robert D. Richardson, Jr. Professor of English, University of Denver (entire); Max Schroeder, Black-Footed Ferret Recovery Team Coordinator, U.S. Fish and Wildlife Service (black-footed ferret); Paul Schullery, author of *American Bears* and *The Bears of Yellowstone* and formerly Park Historian, Yellowstone National Park (grizzly bear); Chris Servheen, Grizzly Bear Recovery Team Coordinator, U.S. Fish and Wildlife Service (grizzly bear); Judy Sheppard, Terrestrial Nongame Wildlife Specialist, Colorado Division of Wildlife (entire); Dave Stevens, Park Biologist, Rocky Mountain National Park (gray wolf).

Also helpful along the way were: Dave Brown, author of *The Grizzly in the Southwest* and *The Wolf in the Southwest*, and Game Branch Supervisor for the Arizona Game and Fish Department; John Craighead, grizzly bear researcher and Executive Director of Wildlife-Wildlands Institute, Missoula, Montana; Art Dimeo, Assistant District Ranger, Conejos District, Rio Grande National Forest, La Jara, Colorado; John Rawinski, Soil Scientist, Rio Grande National Forest, Monte Vista, Colorado; Al LeCount, Chief Bear Biologist, Arizona Game and Fish Department; John Torres, Central Regional Manager, Colorado Division of Wildlife; Ernie Wilkinson, former government trapper, Monte Vista, Colorado; Sandy Binker, Public Affairs Coordinator, Colorado Woolgrower's Association.

The University of Colorado Museum provided valuable access to reference collections, as did the Denver Natural History Museum. Special thanks to Karen Meany, Curator of Mammals at the Denver Natural History Museum.

Amaranth Photos of Boulder provided a discount on photographic development because of the subject and the nonprofit nature of the project.

I would particularly like to thank the following individuals for donating photographs used in the book: Dave Brown, Tim Clark, Linda Elinoff, Bill Ervin, Susan Goldstein, Jim Halfpenny, and Greg Hayes. Also, the Division of Wildlife provided several photographs, and I am grateful for their assistance.

Both Rita Green, the librarian at the Division of Wildlife's Denver Office, and Judy Kayser, the librarian at the U.S. Fish and Wildlife Service's Denver Regional Office, were most helpful. They made my visits both pleasant and productive.

I am grateful to KMGH-TV, Channel 7, the CBS affiliate in Denver, for planning to produce the wildlife documentary based on this book. In particular I would like to thank Lisa Dietsch, Documentary Producer, Tom Kroll, Director of Special Projects, and Caroline Schomp, Assistant News Director.

I would like to thank the following individuals, who consented to be interviewed: Bob Ralston, Executive Vice President, Colorado Cattlemen's Association; Jim Ruch, Director of the Colorado Division of Wildlife; and Tim Schultz, Chairman of the Colorado Wildlife Commission.

Finally, I would like to thank my parents for all of their encouragement, guidance, and support, and to my father in particular for donating his picture of the black bear, taken out the car window on our first trip to Yellowstone years ago.

Foreword

You may never see a live grizzly bear, or wolverine, in your lifetime. You probably won't see one in Colorado, but—you might. That is what this book is all about, what the future holds in this state for six fascinating animals; three probably gone, two possibly gone, and one hopefully being reintroduced successfully.

As the Director of the Colorado Division of Wildlife, the agency charged by the people with the responsibility for perpetuating the fish and wildlife resources of the state—I am troubled by John Murray's book. I do not agree with everything he says, nor do the professional wildlife biologists who work with me agree in every detail. That is no matter, because Murray is right in his key premise. Whether any of these six species will live, free and wild in Colorado, depends solely upon the wishes and the will of the people of Colorado.

You may love grizzly bears—or hate them as some do—or wolves or wolverines. In any case, read this book before you go into battle with one another. Despite his strong self-confessed bias, Murray has done a fine job of summarizing the history, condition, needs, and the arguments surrounding each of these species in Colorado. He fairly presents both sides of the argument about their futures—and then comes down clearly on the animals' side.

More importantly, if you haven't ever thought about it much and have never placed a concern about these animals in very high priority, if you are neither a hunter whose dollars fund nearly all the wildlife management in this state, nor one of the few conservationists who annually check off a few dollars for nongame wildlife on their state income tax form, then pause for a moment, read, and consider.

Establishing and maintaining a significant self-supporting population of any of these six mammals will cost a great deal. It will cost money for land and water—habitat—to support them, and effort, and acrimony and opposition from those who feel they have something important to lose if the measures needed to obtain and maintain these animals are taken.

It is a cost that is clear to John Murray. Because he knows that it is a cost that must be paid if these animals are to have a future, he has made a commitment to match his convictions. He is contributing his royalties from sales of the book to the nongame program in Colorado in order to encourage public interest and support.

In the face of such a generous gesture, I am, more than ever, troubled by this book. Why? Because I fear that not enough people in Colorado care enough to do what needs to be done, to convince the majority of the citizens, and the legislature and the public and private land and water owners of the importance of the investment that John Murray rightly recognizes must be made.

I am troubled because I know what it would mean to me someday, in some Colorado wilderness to suddenly, surprisingly come face to face with a wolverine or lynx standing in my trail, to hear a timber wolf on the ridge behind my elk camp, or to watch from a forested saddle, "Old Ephraim" rooting up sweet grass tubers from a meadow in my mountains.

James B. Ruch, Director
Colorado Division of Wildlife

Preface

On the map it appears as a blue kidney-shaped lake near the headwaters of the Conejos River in the southern San Juan Mountains of Colorado. If you look closely enough you can see a small island near the eastern shoreline. Elevation at the lake, called simply Blue Lake, is 11,463 feet. It is bordered on the west by a mass of tight contour lines, indicating precipitous slopes and dramatic cliffs. Elsewhere, the contours are few and widely spaced, denoting more gently rolling terrain. Across the map, green shaded areas alternate with white areas, representing forested and unforested regions. On the topographic sheet it looks similar to many high-altitude lakes in the Rockies, but it is distinctive in a historic way. To students of endangered species, the place is well known: On September 23, 1979, an adult female grizzly bear was killed there by a bow hunter.

After finishing the first draft of this book, I visited the place in August, 1986. I had spent many long hours in the library and at the typewriter, and I needed a brief respite (and some fresh inspiration) before completing the final revisions. Besides, summer was down to its last few weeks, and I never let the season pass without spending a week or two in the mountains. My base camp was six miles up the South Fork of the Conejos River, where the Canon Verde has its confluence with the main stream. It is another six miles from there to Blue Lake. On the first night, with several hours of daylight remaining, I hiked up into the Canon Verde, following a compass heading off the trail shortly after crossing the South Fork. It seemed the best way to get into an area where people don't often venture, which is where I like to be. As I neared the crest of the first ridge, I thought I heard a waterfall on the far side and, despite the steep grade, hurried to the top. The San Juans are wet mountains, and they are known for their fine waterfalls. But I was fooled by the aspen. There was a large stand of *Populus tremuloides* on the other side, and the sibilant leaves produced a loud *shhhhhhhhh* in the breeze, a sound like the rush of falling water.

The headwaters of the Navajo River in the South San Juan Wilderness Area. The view is from the 11,700 foot ridgeline one half-mile southwest of Blue Lake, looking northwest into the Navajo headwater region. Highest elevation on the alpine ridge in the far background is 12,400 feet. On September 23, 1979 outfitter Ed Wiseman killed an adult female grizzly bear in the spruce-fir stand on the upper right. This is one of the most remote locations in Colorado; it is twelve miles down the South Fork of the Conejos River to the nearest road, which is unpaved. *John Murray*

There was something different about this grove, though. The trees were very big and old, some of the largest and most beautiful specimens I have ever seen. Despite the remote location, some had names, towns, and dates carved on them, a sign that others, possibly fishermen and elk hunters, had been there before. Ordinarily I don't read such things, but the vintage of these intrigued me and I stopped. As might be expected, four of the five I found were Spanish surnamed—the San Luis Valley has been the cradle of Hispanic culture in Colorado for almost three hundred years: *S. Valdez. 1927. Antonito, Co.; Ernie Montoya. La Jara. 44; Victor Archuleta. 7–24–52. Conejos; Lupe Salazar. Taos. 9–72; Dean Faulkner. Tulsa. Octo. 78.*

The dates resonated with some important associations. In 1927, for example, the last pack of wolves in Colorado left the San Juans and drifted south into New Mexico, roaming the Carson National Forest for two years before the U.S. Biological Survey eradicated them. In 1944 the deadly predacide Compound 1080 came into use on the prairies, helping to bring about the demise of the black-footed ferret. In 1952, two years before I was born, a government trapper killed a grizzly at the head of the Los Pinos, the last confirmed killing in Colorado for twenty-seven years. In 1972 the Colorado Division of Wildlife initiated a nongame management program, the first state to do so. That same year a rare lynx was trapped on Guanella Pass near Mt. Evans. In 1978 two wolverines were released by Stouffer Productions, a film production company, near Aspen. Also in 1978, seven river otters were released in Rocky Mountain National Park as part of the river otter recovery plan.

The breeze left the ridge and a solemn evening hush fell on the aspen grove. Somewhere nearby a Townsend's solitaire twittered mournfully. The cold white trunks carried their inscriptions like so many tombstones on the darkening slope, and it seemed I had stumbled on some forgotten cemetery. I was standing there, reflecting on what we have done and are doing, both good and bad, to the mountains and to the wildlife, when something caught my eye. I couldn't tell, at first, what it was. I slowly worked my way through the waist-high cow parsnip over to the base of an enormous aspen, a venerable tree with the girth of a mature Douglas fir, a size unknown elsewhere for the aspen, but not unusual for the species in the cool, wet, undisturbed environment of the high San Juans.

Reaching up, I could just touch the lower edges of the markings. There, a good six feet up, torn deeply into the dusty white trunk, were the ancient black-encrusted claw marks of a bear. There were three distinct sets of them, and they ran together for a foot down the trunk. These were not the neatly spaced razor-cut claw marks of a black bear as it shimmies up or down a tree. These were the purposeful cuttings, the indelible signature, of a very large bear. How long had they been there? I wondered. For how many years more would they remain? Had they been left by a grizzly? Considering the likely size of the animal, and guessing the span of the forepaws, I couldn't help but think it had been a grizzly. The bear had wandered into the same grove as I had, and had felt impelled to leave its mark too, though higher than a man with a knife could reach. It occurred to me as I stood there looking up at those impressive marks that a book has its origins in much the same impulse.

The next day I reached Blue Lake while the sun was still bright in the east. A marmot whistled as I entered the lower meadow around the lake, and by the time I saw them, two magnificent mule deer bucks were already disappearing into the timber. As with most places you discover on a map and dream over while it snows, Blue Lake fulfilled all my expectations. I spent the rest of the day exploring the area, concentrating most of my efforts at the headwaters of the Navajo River, a narrow plunging canyon that opens widely as it spreads to drain the tundra at the Continental Divide. I found much bear sign old and new, but no sign of Old Ephraim. That was fine. Ghosts don't generally leave much evidence behind.

Toward evening, a lively hailstorm came crackling in over the Divide and drove me back down the canyon to camp. With dry kindling I had stored under a spare poncho, I quickly built a small fire. Dinner consisted of South Fork brook trout, foil-wrapped baked potatoes, baked beans, pita bread, and wild raspberries (I gave up on freeze-dried lightweight food ten years ago). There was even a cold can of beer plucked from its hiding place in the river. I retired to the sound of a gentle rain falling steadily on the tent fly.

After a while the rain stopped and a great silence filled the canyon. The moon came out behind the last retreating clouds of the storm, and a family of coyotes began to sing nearby. I stuck my head outside the tent to listen to them, and found the air filled with the fresh scent of wet pine needles. As I lay there gazing up at the stars, I wondered about the future

Grizzly bear cub. *William Ervin*

of the wilderness and the wildlife in Colorado. It seemed to me both were equally endangered in our rapidly changing world. I wondered, too, if this book, or any book, could really hope to have an impact, given the magnitude of the forces that are at work. But then I thought back to some lines Rachel Carson wrote to a close friend as she neared completion of her manuscript *Silent Spring*:

> The beauty of the living world I was trying to save has always been uppermost in my mind . . . I have felt bound by a solemn obligation to do what I could—if I didn't at least try I could never again be happy in nature.

Like Carson, I realized I was bound by a "solemn obligation." I knew I wouldn't be happy in nature until my task was done.

As far as the publisher and I know, this book provides a new organizational format for works of natural history. Whether it does or doesn't though, we believe it follows a paradigm that could be applied to other states, regions, and parts of the world. In Florida, for example, a book on the endangered mammals would include such diverse species as the Florida panther, Caribbean manatee, Key Vaca raccoon, Everglades mink, black bear, fox mangrove squirrel, and key deer. A similar work for Texas would include several of the rare cats—jaguar, jaguarundi, ocelot, and margay—as well as interesting species such as the red wolf, gray wolf, desert bighorn sheep, black-footed ferret, Caribbean manatee, and four species of whale. A regional book for southern Europe would focus on the European brown bear, gray wolf, Spanish lynx, Mediterranean monk seal, Corsican red deer, and Apennine chamois. The author there would also have a choice of three languages. It is to be hoped that some of these books will be written. There is as urgent a need for them in their respective areas as there is for this one in Colorado.

Each chapter in this book is divided into four sections: Introduction, Past History, Natural History, and Current Status and Future Recovery. The book documents all six mammals that are currently listed as either Threatened or Endangered by the state or federal government. Species listed as Endangered for Colorado by the Colorado Wildlife Commission are the river otter, lynx, and wolverine. The federally listed species, designated by the Secretary of the Interior, are the grizzly bear (Threatened in the lower forty-eight states), gray wolf (Endangered in the lower forty-eight states), and black-footed ferret (Endangered in the lower forty-eight states). There are also five "species of special concern" recognized by the Division of Wildlife: the meadow jumping mouse, the olive-backed jumping mouse, the Brazilian free-tailed bat, the kit fox, and the Gunnison prairie dog. These species may become Threatened or Endangered in the future, but are not currently listed.

The first three sections of each chapter concentrate essentially on factual information. With few exceptions, most scientists agree on such things as vital statistics, past history of the species, and general natural history. In the final section of each chapter, however, we will enter some areas of considerable debate as preservation and restoration are examined. It is one thing to write about Ernest Thompson Seton's Lobo of Currumpaw. It is quite another to look at the reintroduction of the gray wolf in Rocky Mountain National Park. Both the grizzly bear and the gray wolf evoke strong feelings, depending on one's point-of-view. Both species are probably extirpated in the state. Opponents of restoration, while often conceding the importance of saving other endangered species, argue that we have so altered the environment in Colorado that the ideal of recovery for the grizzly and wolf is fundamentally unattainable. Proponents of restoration say that we have the habitat and the scientific capability for these projects, and that recovery should be undertaken, primarily for biological reasons.

The wolverine and the lynx offer a different situation, a kind of middle ground between a noncontroversial species like the otter, and a controversial species like the grizzly. For one thing, both species possibly exist in relict numbers in the state, which helps their case for recovery. Opponents of lynx and wolverine restoration argue that both were peripheral species in Colorado, animals at the southern limit of their habitat and range in the Rockies. They question the value of a commitment here. Proponents of lynx and wolverine restoration say that because these animals were an original part of the biota in Colorado, and because we still have the habitat and the ability to restore them, we should undertake their recovery. These two species probably have a better chance for recovery than either the grizzly or the wolf.

As most people in Colorado know, there has been an active river otter recovery program underway in three of the state's rivers for over ten years. It now appears the plan has achieved some of its original objectives. Complete recovery is still in the future, however, and won't be complete until scientists can document that these are self-sustaining and viable populations.

The situation for the black-footed ferret, one of the world's most critically endangered mammals, is bleak but not entirely hopeless. Although the total black-footed ferret population, both in the wild at Meeteetse, Wyoming, and in that state's captive breeding program, may be less than two dozen, this does not mean the ferret will become extinct. The whooping crane population reached a low of fourteen birds in 1939. Today there are more than sixty birds in the wild. There have been no confirmed sightings of black-footed ferrets in Colorado for many years, but possible sightings are still occasionally reported.

Colorado is a miniature of the world. What is currently happening here—the unprecedented growth and development and consequent loss of habitat and species—is happening all over the globe. As the state continues to grow in population and to diversify economically, competing and often incompatible demands are being placed on our finite natural resources. A difficult choice has arisen: How can we strike a balance between a future of prosperity and the fragility of nature? Like a Zen koan, the paradoxical question asked by the Buddhist master of his student, this dilemma challenges our world and our time. Nowhere is it more evident than in the historic struggle, both locally and globally, to save endangered and threatened species. I hope this book will contribute something of value to the dialogue.

Let us turn now and examine the history and habits, lives and fates, myths and realities of these six beautiful and fascinating mammals. "Man is not rational," the Greek philosopher Heraclitus once wrote, "there is intelligence only in what encompasses him." These six animals are each a unique part of that elegant, law-filled order of life that somehow, against all odds, evolved on this world, and that now ironically finds itself threatened by one of its own creations, humankind.

John A. Murray
December 1986
Denver, Colorado

I

ENDANGERED SPECIES

AN INTRODUCTION

The Congress finds and declares that various species of fish, wildlife, and plants in the United States have been rendered extinct as a consequence of the economic growth and development untempered by adequate concern and conservation . . . It is further declared to be the policy of Congress that all Federal departments and agencies shall seek to conserve endangered species and threatened species.
—Endangered Species Act, 1973

The decline of wildlife species has been, and will continue to be, one of the vital environmental issues of our time, both regionally and internationally. All around the world people are becoming more aware of the importance of preserving the diversity of life forms around them, from the last three hundred gavial crocodiles of the Ganges River basin in India, to the last few aye-ayes, a small lemur now protected on a nature reserve in Madagascar. Some faunal species, such as the California condor and the black-footed ferret, are dangerously close to extinction. Others, such as the Mexican wolf and red wolf, have a good chance of being saved through existing gene pools and captive breeding programs, and of then being restored to wild areas where they can be protected. Still others, like the American alligator, eastern timber wolf, trumpeter swan, whooping crane, southern sea otter, northern elephant seal, San Joaquin kit fox, key deer, bison, and musk ox, to name just a few, have been brought back successfully from the edge, and offer us solid hope for the future.

HISTORICAL BACKGROUND

Most scientists agree that the rate of extinction has increased significantly over the last one hundred years, and that it has closely paralleled the unprecedented growth and spread of the human race. In what Desmond Morris, writing in *The Naked Ape*, called its sudden "rags to riches" rise, humankind has extended its influence and dominion over all of nature's provinces and zones, altering large portions of the Earth through inhabitation and cultivation, and often replacing native flora and fauna with its own domesticated species. While civilization and technology, humankind's two greatest achievements, have accomplished much of value, they have exacted a significant ecological price. The concentration of populations in urban centers, the development of fossil fuel and nuclear energy sources, and the widespread use of pesticides in surrounding rural areas, have increasingly polluted the environment, with toxic and radioactive materials now found in the most remote locations of the planet. Jacques Cousteau reported effects in Antarctica, where he found penguins killed by toxic chemicals borne on the ocean currents. More recently, polar bears living in the high Arctic have been found by Canadian scientists to contain a wide variety of toxic chemicals, including DDT, polychlorinated biphenyls, and the pesticides chlordane and toxaphene. Synthetic chemicals, one of the many technological spin offs of the Second World War, now pervade the biosphere. Even more toxic radioactive materials, such as those recently released in the Chernobyl accident, are equally ubiquitous. As a result of all this activity, more than seventy mammalian species and subspecies have become extinct in this century so far, compared with twenty-seven in the nineteenth century, eleven in the eighteenth century, and only seven in the seventeenth century. Each represented, as former Secretary of the Interior Stewart Udall once put it, one of the "end-twigs of the enormous Tree of Life, ever-growing, now over three billion years of age." Each is gone forever.

To put this current rate of extinction in further perspective, consider the following, written by Steven Yaffee in his recent book *Prohibitive Policy, Implementing the Federal Endangered Species Act*:

> . . . and in one 3,000-year period of the Pleistocene, during which great numbers of organisms perished, North America lost about 50 mammalian species and 40 birds — or about 3 species per hundred years. By way of contrast, since the arrival of the Puritans at Plymouth Rock in 1620, over 500 species and subspecies of native animals and plants have become extinct. This averages out to a loss of about 1.4 species per year.

While Yaffee is quick to acknowledge that these data are somewhat mis-leading, because taxonomy has improved with precision over time and be-cause paleofauna are less well known than are present species, it is clear that the general rate of extinction has increased, and that the trend is pri-marily related to human processes. As he concludes, "The net rate is . . . an unprecedented occurrence over geologic time when global climate has been stable."

An argument is sometimes made that these extinctions are part of a larger natural process similar, in a sense, to the mass extinctions of the Cretaceous or Pleistocene. As Yaffee observes:

> This argument builds on ecological niche theory and suggests that the human species is doing exactly what every species strives for (and ecological succes-sion is fueled by): expanding its niche and ensuring its qualitative and quanti-tative growth. Clearly, *Homo sapiens* has broadened its niche dramatically over time.

This scheme attempts to put humankind back into the "natural" scheme of things: if humankind is a part of nature, how can its actions be con-sidered "artificial"? Yaffee challenges this line of thinking:

> The humans-as-purely natural argument can be countered by two types of arguments. One maintains that human well-being is tied to the health of the ecological community. The second argues that humans are fundamentally different from other species—having the capacity to reason and make choices—and thus have a responsibility to other life forms.

Additionally, this sort of reasoning can be, and has been, used as a justification for unregulated development and commercial exploitation of the environment. While extinction is certainly a natural part of evolution, that being caused by man is not, and it is proceeding in some areas (such as the tropics) too rapidly to measure and analyze accurately.

ARGUMENTS FOR PRESERVATION

In *Prohibitive Policy*, Steven Yaffee provides three general reasons to pre-serve endangered and threatened species: human utility, ecosystem stability, and ethics. This is a useful schemata that has been adapted and augmented here as follows: practical value, ecosystem stability, ethical, economic, aes-thetic, theological, and legal. Those who have lobbied in the United States and elsewhere for stronger prohibitive endangered species laws have made their case by utilizing all of these arguments. At issue in each instance has been the irreversibility of extinction and the uncertainty of its consequences.

THE PRACTICAL VALUE ARGUMENT

One of the most convincing reasons for preserving endangered species of animals and plants is that they have real quantifiable value to us. Animals and plants serve humankind in a multitude of ways. As Yaffee writes:

> Species serve humans as food sources, industrial inputs, medicine and drug sources, aesthetic resources, pollution indicators, and as part of a network that provides ecological stability, guaranteeing human survival through the provision of oxygen, the disposal of wastes, the capture of energy, and the recycling of nutrients.

Whether it is penicillin from the lowly fungus *Penicillium notatum* or potatoes au gratin from the common Idaho potato, antitumor alkaloids developed from the rare Madagascar periwinkle or nonaddictive pain killers extracted from poisonous snake venom, the network of animals and plants collectively forms the basis for human life.

The number of plants used as food sources is microscopically small. It has been estimated that only fifty of the world's eighty thousand edible plants have been widely cultivated, and that, in Yaffee's words, ". . . a total of 12 now produce 90 per cent of the world's food supply." The testing and use of indigenous species could have far-reaching agricultural and economic benefits for various parts of the world, particularly in undeveloped countries and in areas dependent on monoculture (the cultivation of a single crop).

Current research in the United States, for example, indicates that the buffalo gourd, a wild squash-like plant native to the semi-arid Southwest, could be grown successfully in the entire region overlying the Ogallala aquifer. The gourd requires little water, and all parts of the plant, including the roots, vines, and seeds, can be put to some use. Further, the gourd may be a source of liquid fuels. Preliminary investigations show that it is capable of good annual yields of an oil that can serve as diesel fuel and as a source of ethanol. If the Ogallala aquifer eventually loses its ability to support current crops, and farmers must seek an alternative product, a plant once considered a useless weed of the desert canyons could become widely cultivated. And this is just one of many examples.

Additionally, it has been estimated that only five per cent of all plant species have been examined for possible use as pharmaceuticals. Yet each year more and more plants become extirpated or extinct, particularly in tropical areas, where the species-rich rain forests are being lost at an alarming rate, forests that also provide a large amount of the oxygen in the Earth's atmosphere.

Animals also have practical value to us. Primates, for example, some of which are threatened in parts of their historic range, are frequently used in medical experiments as surrogates for humans. In the earliest stages of space flight, scientists placed chimpanzees and dogs into space capsules to determine if humans could survive the rigors of rocket launch, zero gravity, and re-entry. Bats and dolphins have given science insight into sonar. Physiologists study the metabolism of the black bear for insights into the problems of cholesterol and kidney disease. The bear's ability to enter a deep sleep resembling true hibernation also intrigues researchers, and could one day help science replicate the same state of suspended animation in human astronauts. The desert pupfish tolerates extremes of salinity and temperature that could have implications for our treatment of human kidney disease. It has recently been discovered that molluscs—clams, snails, mussels—rarely, if ever, get cancer. Yaffee reports that a substance derived from molluscs can prevent or delay cancer in mice, and has had no negative effects when placed *in vitro* with human cells. Who knows which of the threatened or endangered species, from the lowliest and least known to the most commonplace and familiar, might be of use to us in the future?

The industrial and commercial uses of animals and plants are widespread and well known: yeast, gum, rubber, latex, fibers, sponge, oil. Microbes and aquatic insect larvae are utilized in the treatment of human sewage. Manatees (sea cows) have been used in the canals of Florida to remove the water hyacinth, an exotic to the region that now threatens to clog vital inland waterways. Canaries were once taken down into mines to test for the presence of poisonous gases. During World War I, slugs were used as a means of detecting mustard gas. Animals and plants can also serve humankind as living indicators of the health of ecosystems. The decline of raptors, first brought to national attention in 1962 by Rachel Carson in her book *Silent Spring*, alerted us to the dangers in chlorinated hydrocarbon pesticides such as DDT. More recently, the development of skin cancers in various birds and mammals in the Antarctic region has led scientists to the discovery of a massive hole in the Earth's ozone layer. It is believed this disruption in the ozone, a layer vital in blocking the sun's deadly ultraviolet rays, is caused by CFC's—chlorinated fluorocarbons—that are used in aerosols (now banned in the United States but widely used elsewhere) and in refrigerants (such as are found in your automobile's air conditioner).

The practical value of plants and animals to humankind is indisputable. Only the issue of their preservation remains in doubt. None would argue that we could exist without the diversity of life around us, but some would have us believe that a slow attrition does not make an ineluctable trend. These same utilitarians would do well to consider that the ultimate utility is that which forms the basis for life.

THE ECOSYSTEM STABILITY ARGUMENT

A powerful argument in favor of preserving threatened and endangered species is that which says the biosphere is composed of a vast and little understood network of interdependent relationships. As Yaffee writes:

> Most ecologists agree that ecosystems move through very patterned direc-
> tions as they mature. Mature ecosystems are typically highly diverse, with
> many species with narrow niches and intricate connective pathways. It is
> generally agreed that diversity provides stability in that catastrophic events,
> such as climatic changes and disease, are more readily absorbed. The exact
> relationship between diversity and stability is still in controversy. The most
> diverse ecosystem on earth, the tropical forest, is very sensitive to human
> disruption, while the simpler temperate zone forest is quite adaptive. Never-
> theless, the general direct relationship . . . seems to hold: With reduced di-
> versity comes instability.

He gives as an example the importance of the American alligator to the stability of the Florida Everglades. As part of their behavior, alligators dig extremely large holes in their home territory. During periods of drought, these wallowing holes, and the water-filled trenches to nesting areas which alligators also keep open, help birds and fish to survive.

Opponents argue that any one species probably has a marginal value in terms of the ecosystem as a whole. This may be true, but we have no way of determining when the "threshold of stability" is crossed, and when the cumulative effects of a steady attrition attain their catastrophic climax. Additionally, the ranking of species according to their apparent importance in the natural order is a risky affair, fraught with the dangers of any judgment based on human-centered values. Probably more attention should be given to protecting critical ecosystems than to individual species. The loss of species is just the most conspicuous symptom of a larger, and more deadly, affliction. In fact, some individuals and groups have begun to call for a "National Biosphere Reserve system" similar in organization and inspiration to the National Park system, the National Forest system, and the National Wilderness system. One of its strongest advocates is the writer Thomas McNamee, author of *The Grizzly Bear*. McNamee and others believe we should preserve certain natural areas in their organic unity, such as the Glacier National Park/Bob Marshall Wilderness Area Ecosystem, the Greater Yellowstone Ecosystem, and the Grand Canyon Ecosystem. This system of biosphere reserves could, if distributed among the roughly two hundred biotic communities found worldwide, go a long way toward attaining and sustaining global ecosystem stability. It would probably help to abate the general trend toward extirpation and extinction, particularly in the tropics. The core of the pathology, however, is regional overpopulation, and it would have to be addressed if the global objective were to have a reasonable chance of succeeding.

THE ETHICAL ARGUMENT

The first instance of a concern for the sanctity and singularity of each living species occurs in the story of Noah, in which a virtuous man was commissioned by God to preserve examples of all of life as a flood was unleashed to purge iniquity from the world. This parable suggests a moral responsibility toward animals and acknowledges that they are sacred in their own right as fellow creations of an original, and still powerful, creative force. Elsewhere in the Old Testament, Ezekiel, Jeremiah, and Isaiah asserted or implied that the despoliation of the land was not only undesirable but also morally wrong. Traditionally, however, the preservation of wildlife and wild lands has been an issue far removed from ethics, a branch of philosophy dealing with the moral duties and obligations between and among men and women in human society.

In the twentieth century, a few thinkers have begun to suggest that our historic system of ethics should be extended to include our relationships with other organisms, and even with the inanimate processes and features of the natural world. Chief among these is Aldo Leopold, a pioneering conservationist who wrote about his beliefs in the seminal essay entitled "The Land Ethic." Leopold observed that the first ethics, as expressed in the Ten Commandments, dealt with relations between individuals. Later, as we matured, ethics began to deal with the relations between individuals and society. The Golden Rule—Do unto others as you would have them do unto you—integrated the individual with society. At a later date, modern democracy and representative institutions integrated social organization and government with the individual. Leopold proposed that a new ethic needed to be developed, "dealing with man's relation to land and to the animals and plants which grow upon it." As he wrote,

> All ethics so far evolved rest upon a single premise: that the individual is a member of a community of interdependent parts . . . The land ethic simply enlarges the boundaries of the community to include soils, waters, plants, and animals, or collectively: the land.

It is interesting to note that in the philosophy and religion of many native American cultures the same reverence for life is found, as well as the belief in the unity of all living and nonliving things.

While a reverence for life may seem self-evident, its codification is not. What Leopold postulated may be true, but it has yet to be given a firm legal basis. Only recently have the courts begun to acknowledge the "existence value" of wildlife and wild places, a phrase coined in the 1974 case *Minnesota Public Interest Research Group v. Butz*. In that case, the U.S. Forest Service was challenged for not preparing an environmental impact statement before cutting timber in northern Minnesota, as is mandated by the National Environmental Policy Act of 1969. Years may pass before Leopold's land ethic is given comprehensive legal expression. He recognized that it might be a long process when he wrote in 1949: "I regard the present conservation movement as the embryo of such an affirmation [of the land ethic]."

In writing of the land ethic, of an area of morality not yet addressed by the law, Leopold aligned himself with such thinkers as the Roman Stoics, who believed there was a natural law superseding civil law, and with the scholastic theologian Thomas Aquinas, who wrote in *Summa Theologia* that there was an "eternal law" that subsumed both natural and civil law. He is saying that, not only do we have a clear set of natural rights and responsibilities among people, the social contract set forth by Locke, Hume, and Rousseau in the eighteenth century, but we also have an even more fundamental and important ethical relationship with the land. The land ethic affirms the right of all living things to have a "continued existence in a natural state," as Leopold wrote. It says in effect that a river drainage has inalienable rights; that an animal should have a say, if only among its human representatives, in its future; and that even the insensible air has a right not to be violated.

Opponents maintain that it is ridiculous to grant rights to nonhuman organisms, or, worse, to nonliving features and aspects of our world. They believe unequivocably that humankind is the master of all life, with no obligations other than to itself and its own species. They stress the biological imperative—the primal duty to survive and endure—as the guiding principle for human life. Such thinking ignores the rational singularity of *Homo sapiens* and the responsibilities implicit in intelligence, and the ability to feel love, forgiveness, and compassion. Like all ethical axioms, the land ethic must now stand the test of time, the ultimate test of all human ideas, as Einstein observed in his last book, *Out of My Later Years*:

> Ethical axioms are found and tested not very differently from the axioms of science. Truth is what stands the test of experience.

THE AESTHETIC ARGUMENT

In his book *Lives of Game Animals*, Ernest Thompson Seton wrote of the grizzly: "[it is] a magnificent animal, whose extinction would be just such a loss to zoology as the destruction of St. Peter's would be to the world of art." In a similar sentiment, John Muir once wrote that the damming of Hetch Hetchy Valley in the High Sierras would be tantamount to damming a great cathedral:

> Dam Hetch Hetchy! As well dam for waterworks the people's cathedrals and churches, for no holier temple has ever been consecrated by the heart of man.

Both struck a similar note: that the natural creations of this world should be accorded the same high honor and praise we give the creations of the human mind.

The supreme creative forces that brought a grizzly bear into being or that shaped a Grand Canyon make them as worthy of preservation as Beethoven's *Pastoral* symphony, or the odes of Keats, or the paintings of Picasso's "Blue Period." In other words, we should preserve the diversity of life forms, if only because they are beautiful and we have the capacity to appreciate beauty and excellence. Philosophers have long postulated that truth and beauty are perhaps only different words for the same thing. In the words of Keats, concluding his poem "Ode on a Grecian Urn":

"Beauty is truth, truth beauty,"—that is all
Ye know on earth, and all ye need to
know.

Perhaps, in contemplating the majesty of a grizzly bear as it crosses an Alaskan river bar at sunset, or in listening to the timber wolves howl as the moon rises over the Canadian Rockies, we come closer to understanding the truth, and are therefore enriched and ennobled. If nothing else, these animals, and the wilderness they embody, represent a kind of excellence, a perfection of form and function that can only serve to humble and awe the artist—the creator—in all of us.

THE ECONOMIC ARGUMENT

Questions of biology and philosophy aside, endangered species and the pristine regions they inhabit can have a significant hard-dollar value to the people who preserve them. They've known about this in some of the developing and smaller nations for years. Rare and beautiful species, at home in the wild, are very often among their most important economic resources, a priority reflected in the abundance of parks and refuges. Only five per cent of the total land mass of the United States is allocated to parks, wilderness areas, and wildlife preserves. Up to fifteen per cent of the land surface of such countries as Botswana, Zaire, Kenya, Guatemala, Costa Rica, and New Zealand is reserved in this fashion. The fact is, endangered species and their habitats can mean money, and lots of it. People will travel great distances, stay for long periods, and expend large sums, simply to catch a glimpse of a quetzal in a cloud forest, photograph a leopard sleeping in an acacia tree, or spot a polar bear roaming out on the pack ice. Diverse countries have learned through experience that endangered species can be good business, and that capitalism and conservation are not necessarily incompatible. More important, these wild regions are permanent economic resources. Cattle grazing, timber harvesting, slash-and-burn agriculture, and mineral development all extract something from the land they use, and ultimately diminish its quality. In many areas of the tropics, erosion progresses so swiftly that reclamation practices common in the temperate zones are not feasible. President Mobutu Sese Seko of the African Republic of Zaire perhaps put it best in remarks he made several years ago at the opening of his country's parliament:

The heritage of our ancestors is the natural beauty of our country: our rivers, forests, insects, animals, lakes, volcanoes, mountains, and plains. Nature is an integral and real part of our originality and personality. Therefore, we refuse to follow blindly the trend of "developed" countries which want production at any price. We do not believe that peace and happiness are dependent on the number of cars in the garage, the television antennas on the roof, or on the amount of noise in your years. . . . Horror overcomes Zairans when we learn that in a city like New York, people slowly become more and more deaf beginning with the age of 25, whereas a farmer in our country might become so only toward the age of 70. . . . It should not surprise you when we declare that our ambition is to make our country, Zaire, a paradise of nature. . . . We believe that industrialized countries are running the risk at every moment of becoming poorer. We desire only that when scientists have transformed the world into an artificial one, in Zaire an authentic nature will remain. Over the next few years, our national parks will be expanded to over 12 to 15 per cent of the country.

Not all undeveloped nations have followed the course of Zaire. Those that have have made the wiser choice, and have traded quick wealth based on exploitive resource development for long-term economic stability based on nonconsumptive use.

During the past several decades, the United States has seen a dramatic swing from consumptive uses of wildlife (hunting, fishing, and trapping) to nonconsumptive uses of wildlife (bird watching, nature hikes, wildlife photography). According to a recent survey conducted by the U.S. Fish and Wildlife Service and the Bureau of Census, 93.2 million Americans sixteen years and older participated in nonconsumptive wildlife-associated activities in 1980. Total expenditures for nonconsumptive wildlife-associated activities in that same year totaled 14.7 billion dollars. Of this total, 10.7 billion dollars, or seventy-three per cent of the total, was spent on equipment. Travel-related expenditures (food, lodging, transportation) were 4 billion dollars, twenty-seven per cent of the total. A large portion of the approximately 25 million people who visit Colorado each year participate in nonconsumptive wildlife activities, from the annual six thousand who visit the Barr Lake Nature Center to the 2.2 million who visit Rocky Mountain National Park annually. Along the way, they spend a lot of money on a great variety of consumer items: cameras, film, hiking boots, packs, books, food, lodging, gas. Unlike consumptive users, who extract some-

thing—livestock forage, timber, animals, fish, minerals—from the public domain, nonconsumptive users essentially leave the forests, parks, and refuges
as they found them, while still contributing significant amounts of money
to local economies. (Although it is true that, in the narrowest sense, all users
are consumptive, there is an obvious and substantial difference between,
for example, wildlife photographers and big-game hunters.)

Wildlife managers traditionally have focused on the needs of people
involved in consumptive use of game resources because they provided most
of the financial support for agency management. These figures, however,
have led to a reevaluation of this approach. Greater consideration is now
being given to nonconsumptive users of both game and nongame wildlife.
Additional figures from the same study indicate that many of the consumptive users are "dual users," that is to say, they participate actively in nonconsumptive activities as well. Approximately seventy-five per cent of the
consumptive users are dual users, while about forty-two per cent of the nonconsumptive users are dual users. In this context, the preservation of endangered species, and the wild sanctuaries in which they live, can be seen
to be of direct and lasting benefit to the economy of the state. Anything
we can do to enhance the wildness of Colorado will ultimately enrich its
coffers, while at the same time providing a higher quality of life. The further nurturing of parks, refuges, and forests represents an investment in a
future free from the traumatic cycles of "boom and bust" historically associated with consumptive use of state resources, and charts a course into a
stable and prosperous future for our children.

THE THEOLOGICAL ARGUMENT

The theological argument cannot be ignored. For many people, perhaps
even the majority, it is the most persuasive reason for preserving life on
Earth, particularly plants and animals in danger of extinction. This view
postulates the universal holiness of life, the inviolate sanctity of each living
thing, and the necessity of protecting organisms, either as the living embodi-
ments of a creator or creative force, or as the consummate artistry of a
supreme, if inscrutable, creator or creative force. It says, in effect, that as
long as humankind has the power and the ability to save a living thing,
it has the obligation and duty to make certain it is saved.

This view is found in many, if not most, of the world's religions. In
Buddhism, for example, the first of the "Four Great Vows" recited after every
service is the statement: "However innumerable beings are, I vow to save

them." The Upanishads, written in India some three thousand years ago, speak of a ubiquitous supreme being who is literally "within everything," that is "the innermost essence of all that exists." In the Islamic faith, one of the great Sufi ascetics, Ibrāhīm ibn Adham, attained his conversion while out hunting rabbits on his father's estate. After hearing the voice of God condemning this activity, he left his opulent station in life, adopted the simple woolen tunic of the shepherds, and devoted his life to virtue and true understanding.

Probably the most famous individual in the Christian faith to stress the sacredness of living things was St. Francis of Assisi (1182–1226), the Italian founder of the Franciscan order. St. Francis, like Gautama Buddha and Ibrāhīm ibn Adham, was born into a wealthy family, the son of the merchant Ser Pietro de Bernadone. At the age of twenty-five, however, he turned his back on materialism and began to spend his time among the poor and in the wilds of nature, pursuing a life of poverty and contemplation. St. Francis felt a strong sense of kinship with every living thing, and celebrated that in his poems and songs. One legend tells of how he persuaded a youth who had snared some doves to donate them to his monastery, where they were released into the garden. Another tells of how he would preach sermons "to my little sisters," the birds in the forest. On one occasion he tried to convince the emperor Frederick II to make a special law not to "kill our sisters the larks and other birds."

In the twentieth century another monk, Thomas Merton, who spent his life in Gethsemane Abbey, a Trappist monastery in northern Kentucky, was similarly inspired. He also gained worldwide renown as a poet of nature and once wrote, in "The Sowing of Meanings":

> For, like a grain of fire
> Smouldering in the heart of every living essence
> God plants his undivided power—
> Buried His thought too vast for worlds
> In seed and root and blade and flower...

Elsewhere in this century the American poet Robinson Jeffers, writing from his cliff house on the Big Sur coast of California, expressed a similar sentiment:

> Look how beautiful are all the things that He does. His
>   signature
> Is the beauty of things.
>   ("Look, How Beautiful")

•••••

And we know
   that the enormous invulnerable beauty of things
   Is the face of God, to live gladly in its presence, and die without
   grief or fear knowing it survives us.

("Nova")

For some, the theological argument is an irrelevancy. For others, it is the core of belief. Happily, the two often agree on the same end goal – the preservation of species.

THE LEGAL BASIS

To the original inhabitants of this continent, the native American Indians, the land and its wildlife comprised a unified natural community of which they were an organic part. Contrary to popular mythology, however, the tribal homeland *was* considered the property, if only in a communal sense, of the people who lived upon it, and sometimes had to be defended in skirmish or battle from Indian interlopers or invaders. Several examples of this are found in recorded history, but one of the most well-documented incidents occurred in Colorado. The Taos trapper William Drannen described the conflict in his autobiography, *Thirty-one Years on the Plains and in the Mountains*. In 1850, while traveling through South Park, one of several large intermontane parks in Colorado, Drannen and his companion Kit Carson were invited by the Ute Indians to observe an important battle between that tribe, who generally inhabited Western Slope Colorado, and the Comanche, who were more of a plains-dwelling tribe. At issue were the rights to hunt South Park, a game-rich region. After being arranged by tribal diplomats, the battle commenced on a specific location and at a predesignated time. Fought with precise, almost feudal rules of engagement and warrior etiquette, the bloody confrontation lasted from dawn to dusk for three days. It ended only after the Comanche succeeded in crossing the stream that separated the two tribes and overran the Ute camp, the predetermined sign of victory. Humiliated by their defeat, the Ute quietly packed up camp and marched over the Continental Divide, not to return in that generation. This incident, and others like it, indicate that both land and wildlife were considered property long before the *Susan Constant, Godspeed,* and *Discovery* first sighted "the Bay of Chesupiac" on April 26, 1607.

To the Europeans, land was not a community but rather a commodity in which individuals, as well as states, could legally claim ownership. Land, like chattel, could be purchased and sold, inherited and traded, won and lost in the courts. Wildlife was also considered the property of the land-owner. The best game in the rural countryside was often owned by the aristocracy and reserved for their use, a situation that displeased the commoners as well as the middle class. A popular scholarly legend about William Shakespeare, for example, tells that in his youth he often poached deer in the private woodlands of the Warwickshire Arden near Stratford-upon-Avon. This practice is thought to be indicated by these telling lines, taken from one of his first London plays, *Titus Andronicus*:

> What, hast not thou full often struck a doe,
> And borne her cleanly by the keeper's nose?
> (2.1.92–93)

The squatters had no rights against the sovereign under Anglo-Saxon law, but in America the squatter could, and occasionally did, become a form of egalitarian king. Wild nature was the final arbiter of the stature of a person in the New World. A commoner could, with hard work and a few seasons of good fortune, become the landed equal of a lord to the crown. The virgin woods were a place where any person could hunt, fish, trap, explore, or settle. It would be this fierce belief in our independence, symbolized in free land and free wildlife, that would ultimately help to bring about the American Revolution. And it would be our longing for this vanishing frontier in the twentieth century, coupled with a growing awareness of its value for our existence, that would then work to preserve it through conservation legislation.

Throughout the early period, the American wilderness and its wildlife were viewed as the wilds were in biblical times: as an inexhaustible resource provided solely for the use and convenience of humankind and as an earthly chaos threatening the divinely-inspired order of society. If it were not tamed and dominated, it was a useless wasteland and worse—it was feared as the shadowy haunt of the devil. This fear of the wilds, coupled with the longing to tap its riches, would shape American use and abuse of the land and its wildlife for the next two hundred years. As the French writer de Tocqueville was later to observe, we were wasteful in the sudden wealth of our youth, intoxicated by its profusion even as we were evangelical in its subjugation:

Americans do not see the marvelous forests surrounding them until they begin to fall beneath the axe. . . . The American people see themselves marching through wilderness, drying up marshes, diverting rivers, peopling the wilds, and subduing nature.

The first instance of government intervention on behalf of wildlife occurred in 1646, when the leaders of the Virginia colony, responding to complaints about overhunting, ordered the deer season closed. This instance of concern is conspicuously rare in the colonial and expansionist period. The colonies, and later the territories and states, were generally more concerned with subduing the natives and promoting settlement and economic progress. Bounty laws were frequently implemented to eliminate predators, particularly the wolf.

It was not until the early nineteenth century that people began to seriously question prevailing policy and modes of thinking with respect to nature and wildlife. Among the first were the prominent New England writer and philosopher Ralph Waldo Emerson and his friend Henry David Thoreau. Both wrote passionately of the need for a new environmental consciousness, and their writings became very popular. Soon changes became evident. In 1846 Rhode Island briefly closed the hunting season on several waterfowl species during the spring breeding period. In the 1850s, at the then staggering cost of five million dollars, Central Park was established in New York City. In 1858, Henry Thoreau wrote of the need for

. . . national preserves, in which the bear, and the panther, and some even of the hunter race may still exist, and not be civilized off the face of the earth—not for idle sport or food, but for inspiration and our own true recreation.

In 1864 President Lincoln signed a measure preserving the Yosemite Valley "for public use, resort and recreation." This bill, passed largely through the efforts of Frederick Olmsted, the designer of Central Park, was the first scenic nature reserve created by federal action.

The year 1864 also saw the publication of George Marsh's classic work *Man and Nature*, an ardent plea for preservation called by Lewis Mumford "the fountainhead of the conservation movement." Four years later, in 1870, the first government-owned wildlife refuge was established in what is now Lake Merritt, in the heart of downtown Oakland, California. Two years later, on March 1, 1872, President Ulysses Grant signed the bill that forever withdrew the Yellowstone region from the public domain, creating both Yellowstone National Park and an important precedent for conservation. In 1885, inspired by this great new park to the west, the New York state legislature designated the Adirondack Mountains a forest preserve, and in 1892 formally created Adirondack Park, an area larger than Yellowstone and Yosemite combined.

Meanwhile, in the Far West, the great (or terrible) "Age of the Raiders" was finally coming to a close. Americans had, over a fifty-year period, completely conquered a substantial area of the North American continent. With Geronimo's surrender to General Miles at Skeleton Canyon, Arizona on September 3, 1886, the last of the Indian resistance was gone. The native bison of the plains were nearly extinct. The plains grizzly bear and plains wolf *were* extinct. The elk now inhabited only the high mountains. Much of the prairie was homesteaded and even on the most remote alpine ridges, herds of sheep grazed. Cattle grazed the range at lower elevation. Mining and timber industries prospered. Of this period the western writer Wallace Stegner once observed:

> It seems to me significant that the distinct downturn in our literature, from hope to bitterness, took place almost at the precise time when the frontier officially came to an end, in 1890, and when the American way of life had begun to turn strongly urban and industrial.

The death of the frontier brought about the birth of the nostalgic campaign to save it, as conservationists began to lobby Congress for a system of forest reserves. Within a month after the Forest Reserve Act passed in 1891, President Harrison had withdrawn thirteen million acres from the public domain and created fifteen forest reserves. The passing of several species into extinction, including the passenger pigeon, heath hen, and Carolina parakeet, together with the endangered status of other species like the once-plentiful bison, would further awaken the American people and catalyze a much-needed change in thinking.

By the end of the century, the need for a comprehensive federal system for protecting wildlife was recognized. All that was needed was a leader to give birth to the concept. Theodore Roosevelt was that leader. Roosevelt helped the cause of conservation more than any other president (with the possible exception of Jimmy Carter, who created more parks and wilderness areas—in total acreage—than any other president). On March

14, 1903, Roosevelt created the first federal wildlife refuge on Pelican Island, a five-acre rookery for brown pelicans on Florida's east coast. By the time he left office in 1909, there were fifty-three federal wildlife refuges, including six in Alaska. Roosevelt also transferred the forest reserves from the Department of the Interior to the Department of Agriculture, where they were designated National Forests. All totaled, under the original Act of 1891, Presidents Harrison, Cleveland, and Roosevelt set aside 132 million acres, which today comprise the greater part of the national forests of the West.

President Taft approved the first use of federal funds to purchase lands specifically for wildlife by acquiring 12,800 acres in 1909 from the Flathead Indians in Montana for the endangered American bison. In 1913 Congress enacted two historic pieces of wildlife legislation: the Federal Tariff Act, which forbade the importation of plumes and other bird parts except for scientific purposes; and the Weeks-McLean Act, which declared the protection of migratory game birds to be a federal responsibility. Subsequently, the Migratory Bird Treaty Act of 1918 empowered the Biological Survey (a precursor of the U.S. Fish and Wildlife Service) to regulate hunting and establish limits for waterfowl. During the same period, gun and ammunition manufacturers realized the decline in game-bird populations was threatening their business, and began to lobby for strengthened protective laws.

During the 1920s, as motor vehicles became widely used, the situation for wildlife began to deteriorate as road hunting, mining, and logging increased. Preservationists began to grow alarmed at the despoliation of public lands. To save the wildlife and last pristine areas from what some saw as ultimate annihilation. Aldo Leopold, then a young forester with the Forest Service, proposed that wilderness areas be formed, places to be kept forever in their wild state. In 1924, over half a million acres of the Gila National Forest in New Mexico were officially set aside as the Gila Wilderness Area, the first of many that were to follow. Another important figure in this era was Bob Marshall, also a forester with the Forest Service, who suggested the nation develop a comprehensive National Wilderness Preservation System. In September, 1938, a new set of regulations written by Marshall gave the Secretary of Agriculture the power to set aside unbroken tracts of one hundred thousand acres or more as Wilderness Areas and small tracts of five thousand acres or more as Wild Areas.

The drought and Dust Bowl of the 1930s created a crisis situation for many wild animals in the West. One of the responses, in terms of federal action, was the 1934 Federal Duck Stamp Act, which required hunters of waterfowl to buy a one-dollar stamp, with the proceeds going toward habitat improvement and preservation. In 1939 the Bureau of Fisheries, under the Commerce Department, and the Bureau of Biological Survey, under the Agriculture Department, were consolidated and renamed the Fish and Wildlife Service, under the Interior Department.

The first significant account of endangered species in America was the book *Our Vanishing Wildlife*, written in 1913 by New York zoologist and zoo director Dr. William Hornaday. Hornaday made an impassioned plea for an end to the "wanton slaughter" that had devastated many species. More than fifty years later, two major bills were passed by Congress that helped to make Hornaday's dream of nature refuges for endangered species a reality. The first was the Wilderness Act of 1964, which formalized the work of Leopold and Marshall. The second was the Endangered Species Preservation Act of 1966, which, together with the Endangered Species Conservation Act of 1969, made it a crime to import, export, take or otherwise disturb an endangered species. The Endangered Species Act of 1973 is an even more sweeping piece of legislation, containing several new definitions, including Endangered, Threatened, and Critical Habitat. Amendments in 1982 added provisions for the establishment of experimental populations to further the conservation of endangered species. These bills rank as some of the most significant pieces of conservation legislation in our history. They insure that species will have both the necessary habitat and the powerful protection of the federal government in their fight for survival.

Under the Endangered Species Act, approximately 750 animals and well over 3,000 plants have been listed as either Threatened or Endangered in the United States and its territories. It has now become standard procedure for companies and federal agencies to work out any conflicts over endangered species in the earliest planning stages of projects. Between 1979 and 1982 the number of consultations producing written biological opinions by the Fish and Wildlife Service dropped from 968 to 341. During the same period the number of informal consultations rose from 1,585 to 4,321. Environmental Impact Statements, now required by the National Environmental Quality Act of 1969, routinely give close attention to the impact of projects on affected species and critical habitat. This represents a major change in the status quo, with the preservation of rare species finally institutionalized as an accepted part of American growth and development.

We have come a long way since the Virginia Bay Colony first ordered a closed season on white-tailed deer. The *terra incognita* and its "wilde beasts," once feared and subjugated, is now carefully nurtured and protected. While fully aware of our many failures and shortcomings, we can be rightfully proud of the pioneering work our nation has done with respect to wildlife and the wilderness. The world has followed our example in the formation of national parks, wildlife refuges, national forests, and wilderness areas, with such refuges now found from the plains of the Serengeti to the cloud forests of Costa Rica, from the Galapagos Islands of Ecuador to the Apennine Mountains of Italy. Similarly, our endangered species legislation has spawned protective laws and treaties around the world.

THE SITUATION IN COLORADO

Colorado has been considered a national leader in nongame research and management, and in the protection of endangered and threatened species. The nongame management effort began in 1972, and has accomplished much of significance since then, including the River Otter Recovery Project, the reestablishment of the greenback trout in certain waters, stabilizing nesting areas for white pelicans, the hatching and rearing of Colorado River squawfish for planting purposes, the greater prairie chicken transplant, the wolverine and lynx verification project, the grizzly bear verification project, and an extensive survey of declining riparian communities along Colorado's major rivers.

In 1977, House Bill 1390 created the voluntary check-off for nongame wildlife programs on all state income tax forms, a system that has since been adopted by over thirty-six states. Since its inception in 1978, the check-off has raised nearly 4.7 million dollars. In recent years, however, this revenue source has declined, possibly because of the addition of two similar check-offs on the same form (domestic abuse and Olympics). Under the sunset provision of the legislation establishing the nongame check-off, it expires in 1987. Citizen response will no doubt play a major role in the legislature's decision to renew or not to renew this vital source of funding for nongame wildlife programs.

The Colorado Division of Wildlife, unlike other state agencies, is essentially self sustaining, and generates almost all of its operating budget from the sale of hunting and fishing licenses. Less than one per cent of the nongame budget comes from the general fund (only one dollar in 1985–1986 and 1986–1987). Approximately fifty-six per cent of the Division's annual one-million-dollar nongame program budget comes from the nongame check-off. Other major sources of monies include the Dingell-Johnson Act, an excise tax on fishing-related equipment (seventeen per cent), the Pittman-Robertson Act, an excise tax on hunting-related equipment (fifteen per cent), and federal monies provided specifically for endangered species programs.

Expenditures of the annual nongame budget are divided among the management of nongame fish, birds, and mammals as well as community studies and nonconsumptive-use projects. Birds and fish get most of the budget (39 per cent and 40.5 per cent respectively). Nonconsumptive-use projects get around 10 per cent, community studies get 5.5 per cent, and mammals get only 3 per cent (i.e. $30,000 in a one-million-dollar budget). The major emphasis of the Division's nongame effort has been, since 1972, the recovery and protection of endangered and threatened species. Because of declining sources of funding, the Division of Wildlife is currently looking at other creative and innovative methods of raising funds for the nongame programs.

While it is true that floral and faunal species are disappearing at an alarming rate in other parts of the globe, particularly in the tropical hardwood forests, the situation in the northern latitudes, and particularly in Colorado, is not as dire. Much of value has been done to save endangered and threatened species and their critical habitat. Only a very few animals thought to have occurred historically in Colorado are now known to be extinct: Carolina parakeet, yellowfin cutthroat trout, Merriam's elk, Great Plains wolf, southern Rocky Mountain gray wolf, and plains grizzly bear (some of these are subspecies).

Coloradans have much to be proud of in their efforts to maintain the high quality of their environment, but much more needs to be done. Joining in the effort to help endangered species does not necessarily begin, as many believe, at the far ends of the world with glamorous and exotic species like the mountain gorilla, Siberian tiger, or giant panda. It can begin right here, in our own backyard, with the native species that are the subject of this book, and others even more mundane, such as the Johnny Darter of the Platte River just south of Denver, or the prairie sharp-tailed grouse of rural Douglas County along Interstate 25. It can begin with something as ordinary as your state income tax form, or your individual donations to private or public efforts, or your vote on election day, or even the purchase of this book, whose royalties go to the Colorado Nongame Wildlife Fund.

II

WHAT ARE MAMMALS

AND WHERE DID

THEY COME FROM?

When I view all beings not as special creations, but as the lineal descendants of some
few beings which lived long before the first bed of the Silurian system was deposited,
they seem to me to become enobled [sic].
— Charles Darwin, *Origin of the Species*

The biosphere is not a closed system. The Earth is an active participant in
a vast extraplanetary environment. Consequently, the history of life on this
planet, and, more to the point, the history of the class Mammalia and the
order Carnivora cannot be properly understood without a careful examination of the history of the solar system. Recent astronomical and paleonto-
logical discoveries have improved our knowledge of the process of evolution.
Paleontologists have discovered, in the collation and cataloguing of all known
extinct species, that the mass extinction of faunal and floral life on Earth
is cyclic. It occurs on a regular basis approximately every 26 million years.
The last mass extermination was eleven million years ago. The next will
be in about fifteen million years.

   The reason this occurs, according to one of the more widely accepted
astronomical theories, is that a distant shell of comets located at the far edges
of the solar system, a body known as the orc cloud, is periodically disrupted
by a widely roaming companion star to our own sun called Nemesis. This

perturbation of the normal configuration of the orc cloud is so immense that it sends a number of comets hurtling off course in toward the central solar system. Here some of them are destined to collide with the nine planets and their moons. The origin of our own species, and of parent mammalian species, may, then, be as related to events tens of millions of miles from earth as it is to the natural competition among species.

The first primitive mammals arose 150 to 175 million years ago during the Mesozoic era, in the Jurassic period, from a group of mammal-like reptiles known as the *Synapsida*. Probably at least five large groups of Synapsidae developed mammal-like characteristics. These archaic mammals represented an advance over reptiles in several significant ways. First, being warm blooded meant that they, unlike reptiles or amphibians, could occupy cooler, even cold, climates, and develop successful adaptive strategies to cope with the challenges of the cold. Second, the mammals had differentiated teeth, which meant they could masticate their food and prepare it for quick digestion, thus increasing their activity periods. Reptiles, by contrast, swallow their prey whole and may remain inactive for up to a week as the meal is slowly digested. Increased activity among mammals translated into greater ease in escaping reptilian predators and in catching prey. Third, mammals developed an internal diaphragm to control breathing, providing oxygen more efficiently than the reptile's rib-controlled breathing. Finally, mammalian activity was further enhanced by the evolution of a four-chambered heart rather than the three-chambered heart found in all reptiles except the crocodiles. A four-chambered heart separates arterial from venous blood, which helps in the more rapid and efficient use of oxygen and calories.

At the end of the Cretaceous period, 65 million years ago, the ruling reptiles who had dominated the Earth for over 100 million years were almost all wiped out. Scientists were long mystified by this sudden mass extinction until 1979, when geologist Walter Alvarez reported finding a sterile band of clay devoid of fossils in a set of limestone deposits in Italy. It was later found that this band is continuous over a large portion of the planet, and that it corresponds exactly with the Cretaceous-Tertiary boundary, the time of the great extinction. With the assistance of his father Luis Alvarez, a Nobel-prize-winning physicist, Walter Alvarez determined that the clay in this zone was thirty times richer in the rare element iridium than the layers above or below. Iridium is commonly found in asteroids. It is now believed by some that a "nuclear winter" effect generated by the impact of an enormous comet striking the earth was primarily responsible for the environmental changes that precipitated the sudden decline of the widespread and successful reptiles. The worldwide search for the point of impact is now focused upon the enormous Manicouagan Crater in Quebec.

Our ancestors at the time were the most unprepossessing of animals, organisms with the size, instincts, and intelligence of a mole or tree shrew. With the gigantic predaceous reptiles gone, the world stage was cleared for the mammals, who soon diversified exuberantly and flourished, filling virtually every habitat on earth. Mammals today form one of the most important animal groups on earth. They inhabit virtually every ecosystem on the planet. Bats dart and swoop through the air in both hemispheres. Monkeys climb and jump among the trees of tropical and semitropical forests. Whales dive to the depths of the great oceans. Otters swim in the inland lakes and streams. Cheetahs run down wildebeests on the African plains. Polar bears pad across the wastelands of the high Arctic. And *Homo sapiens*, perhaps the most amazing mammal of all, now travels far beyond the Earth in the vacuum of outer space, carrying the legacy of the planet to other worlds.

Mammals are divisible into three subclasses, of which the first and possibly the second is represented in the fauna of Colorado. These are: 1) The Eutheria, containing by far the greatest number of mammals, in which the young are nourished before birth by means of a placenta. The Eutheria are found all over the world; 2) The Metatheria, containing the marsupials, in which the young are born in an early stage of development as a result of the absence of a placenta (an organ in which young mammals are nourished before parturition). These animals are found in Australia and in America. Two species of the marsupial opossum are found in the eastern and south-eastern United States. One possibly occurs in Colorado; and 3) The Prototheria, containing the egg-laying echidna and platypus. These unusual mammals are confined to the Australian region. Of the twelve orders into which the Eutheria are generally divided, only six are found in Colorado. Of these six, one is the Carnivora. All six mammals in this book are carnivores, belonging to several different families, including the Mustelidae (river otter, black-footed ferret, wolverine), the Canidae (gray wolf), the Ursidae (grizzly bear), and the Felidae (lynx).

Colorado is an area important to North American mammals, providing a geographically rich and diverse region where the mammals of the Great Plains, the southwestern deserts, and the Rocky Mountains converge. Approximately 136 species of mammal are found in the ecosystems of the state, which range from the Upper Sonoran environments of the eastern prairie to the alpine tundra of the high mountains.

Early explorers, from the Escalante-Dominguez Expedition to the Pike Expedition, made many notes and observations on the native fauna, but did not attempt a systematic or truly scientific survey. The first such study was conducted by the naturalist Thomas Say, who accompanied the expedition of Major Long into the area of the Front Range in 1820. For the next fifty years, most ecological studies related to military and exploratory activity, including the expeditions of Fremont, Abert, Pope, Bryan, Wheeler, and Hayden.

The first complete listing of Colorado mammals was made by Edward Royal Warren, a mining engineer whose amateur interest in natural history was encouraged by several scientist friends. His work is considered pioneering and consists of three long books and several dozen shorter papers. Merritt Cary is another important figure in the early study of local mammals, and undertook a number of studies and reports dealing primarily with the historic and geographic distribution of Colorado fauna. Since that time, several individuals have been prominent, but none more than David M. Armstrong, a Professor of Natural Science at the University of Colorado, whose classic work *Distribution of Mammals in Colorado* is the definitive source book on all native mammals.

Because of a number of recent and ongoing studies, our knowledge of mammals (and of carnivores) in Colorado has increased greatly, but is still exceeded by our ignorance. Above all, the findings of research biologists need to be consistently incorporated into wildlife-management decisions. The work of scientists does not exist in a vacuum. It must be married to policy and decision making. Only then will science benefit the society that fosters it.

III

DEEP STREAMS

THE RIVER OTTER

> Falstaff: Setting thy womanhood aside, thou art a beast
> to say otherwise.
> Hostess: Say, what beast, thou knave, thou?
> Falstaff: What beast? Why, an otter.
> Prince: An otter, Sir John? Why an otter?
> Falstaff: Why? She's neither fish nor flesh; a man knows
> not where to have her.
> —William Shakespeare, *King Henry IV*, Part I

INTRODUCTION

He swam in a slow and easy motion, with strong regular kicks of his thick
webbed hind feet and even strokes of his smooth round tail, which he used
as a rudder to guide himself through the water. He was cruising upstream
on the North Fork of the Colorado River in Rocky Mountain National
Park, pushing steadily against the current with only his eyes, nose, and ears
showing, beaverlike, above the surface. All his lines were sculpted and swept
back, like a piece of wood that has been in the water a very long time,
a once-tangled branch from which everything irrelevant has been removed,
so that only the simplest of forms, the core of beauty, remains. It was a
lovely slender body with a short muzzle, a broad and flattened head, a
muscular neck and trunk, and a powerful tapered tail trailing behind it to
a point. Everything about him was made for the water, from the head curved
like a river stone, to the tiny ears flattened into the dense fur, to the fur
itself—a luxurious dark brown coat so fluid and fine that it seemed he wore

the very element in which he swam. Only his stiff white whiskers protruded visibly outward from the thick muscular contour of his body, and they offered only passing resistance to the current. To the water he was just another wave gliding through the ever-flowing continuum.

To the biologist from Colorado State University studying the North Fork river otter transplant, he was M31 (male number 31), one of over twenty otters being monitored in the Kawuneeche Valley and its environs. Originally brought to Colorado in 1983, M31 had been surgically implanted with a small three-ounce radio transmitter and then been released into the wild. On a floppy disc back in Fort Collins, all of M31's vital information and sightings were recorded. He had been captured in Minnesota as a juvenile and shared the river with otters from Wisconsin, Michigan, Minnesota, and Washington. Like most, he was a widely ranging free spirit, and had been radio tracked as far east as the headwaters of the North Inlet, just below the feeder stream from Lake Nanita, and among virtually all of the western and northern tributaries of the North Fork. Using an omnidirectional whip antenna and a hand-held "H" antenna, the biologist and his assistants, working from vehicles, on foot, and the air, had patiently tracked M31 and his cousins for three years.

It was an hour before daybreak and the full August moon, still high among the spire-topped spruce and fir, brightened the winding course of the river. In the deep pools where the clear snowmelt gathered behind the rock falls or the log jams, the water was so still that the tall stars could twinkle upon it and the ghostly clouds gliding over the moon. In other places, where the channel narrowed and the water sped over the stones, the splashing water scattered the light into a myriad of steel-like slivers glimmering on the surface of the stream. It was in the pools that the fishing was best for the otter, where the trout gathered and the suckers scavenged and the frogs jumped in now and then.

It had been three days since the hailstorm, and the river was once again clear and moving slowly well below its banks—so clear, that in one deep pool the otter dove to retrieve an aluminum fly box that had fallen to the bottom. On a spruce deadfall still dragging half-green boughs in the water he tried to open it with his dextrous paws, but could not find its secret and left it there, gleaming like a treasure chest in the moonlight. A little farther on he left the water and loped across a grass meadow with the peculiar gait of an otter to an enormous boulder left perched on the gravel by a glacier that retreated long ago. It was marked with fresh and old otter scent, as well as the scent of mink, weasel, bobcat, coyote, and mountain lion. After leaving his scent he returned to the river, spooking a cow moose and her calf along the way, who snorted as he passed.

On either side of the river the mountains rose as steeply as the neck of a horse, looming darkly over the narrow valley. Several of the cataracts and waterfalls streaming down their sides from the high lakes could be heard, surging against the silence. Down lower, in the lodgepole stands and sedge parks, the owls could be heard as they hunted, and the bleats and grunts of the grazing elk. Farther up the valley, near the remote headwaters of the North Fork, there was a treeless gray mass of bedrock and tundra, a formidable mountain as rounded and battered as the canine tooth of an old bear, with a few white patches of lingering snow scattered here and there. A few of the otters released into the valley had already crossed over this mountain and colonized the northern waters. A few more had died from various causes. Most had stayed in and around the valley where they had been released. Even when the big snows came in December, the otters could still fish, seal-like, from holes dug in the ice.

As the otter approached the footbridge over the river to the Never Summer Ranch, once a private inholding in Rocky Mountain National Park, but now a historical exhibit of a classic early twentieth century dude ranch, he slowed and submerged silently. Four body lengths ahead, where the riffle swirled around the rock pilings, he could see a small school of brown trout holding on the gravel bottom, just at the leading edge of the moon shadow cast by the bridge, rising occasionally to take a passing insect. With a quick whip of his tail he accelerated forward and grabbed the last one tightly in his jaws as the others shot upstream. He brought the trout ashore, still flapping wildly, tore it apart on a flat rock and devoured its edible parts, leaving only the head, the back, and the tail for the ravens to find in the morning. Near the spot he scent-marked a familiar boulder and then stood on his hind legs, using his tail for support, and held his front paws against his chest. He was just a half mile below the Timber Creek Campground and could smell the sharp scent of woodsmoke from an early campfire and hear the clang of a coffee pot on a metal grill. He reentered the water and continued upstream toward the beaver ponds where he would rest and sleep during the hot part of the day, keeping to the far side of the river, where blue-winged teal could sometimes be found with their summer broods.

A mile farther on, the otter entered a beaver-pond complex. He stayed on the west side of the valley, carefully avoiding those ponds where several fly fishermen were casting quietly. It was becoming light now, and the last clouds of mist were drifting off the water into the aspen groves as small

River otter. *Colorado Division of Wildlife*

scattered herds of mule deer browsed through the underbrush. The trout were rising on all seven ponds. The otter caught two more trout and passed through three large beaver ponds before he reached his destination, an abandoned beaver lodge. He chased the muskrats from their nest and settled into his favorite daybed for a long rest. Within minutes, he was fast asleep, his nose, eyes, and paws twitching as he dreamed such dreams as otters dream. A half mile to the east, on the side of the road, one of the biologist's field assistants put down the H antenna with which she had identified the otter's general location, and wrote in her spiral notebook: "M31. August 24. 0622. Clear skies. Air temperature 34 Fahrenheit. No wind. Beaver Pond Complex, Above Timber Creek Campground."

I began this book with the river otter because, of Colorado's six endangered mammals, the river otter is in the best shape, and probably will be for some time. I wanted to begin on an optimistic note, with a sense of what we *can* do. The otter is the only endangered mammal in Colorado for which there has been a successful program of reintroduction, a program that will have to be emulated if the other five species are ever to be downlisted or delisted. The otter offers hope that we can go back and repair what we have damaged. It has been returned to the North Fork of the Colorado River (Kawuneeche Valley) in Rocky Mountain National Park, to the Piedra River in the San Juan Mountains, and to the Black Canyon of the Gunnison River near Montrose. Future releases may include some of the desert river systems, including the Green, lower Colorado, and Dolores rivers.

At least one author has suggested that the otter may be more advanced than we commonly think. In his compelling account of evolution and life in the Klamath Mountains of northern California, *The Klamath Knot*, naturalist David Rains Wallace poses an interesting thought. After observing some otters on the Eel River he wrote:

> It is hard to imagine where the evolutionary path of otters will lead . . .
> Tools, curiosity, playfulness, sociability—otters may be the "humans" of sixty million years hence.

Perhaps, perhaps not. At the very least, we see a kinship with the otter and a shared mammalian bond, as well as an irresistible social quality that plainly endears the animal to us.

PAST HISTORY

Because of its aquatic habitat, fossil remains of *Lutra canadensis* are understandably rare. From what is known, it appears that the otters as a distinct race have been around a very long time. An ancestor, *Lutra licenti*, has been traced to the late Miocene. Apparently, the otter moved into the New World between 1.7 and 1.8 million years ago. In North America, fossils are found primarily in the East and the Deep South. Historically, the otter ranged over much of North America north of Mexico. Other species of otter found around the world, and considered in danger of extinction, include the La Plata otter and giant otter of South America, the Cameroon clawless otter of Cameroon, and the southern sea otter, which ranges on the Pacific Coast.

Otters and humankind have a long relationship. One of the earliest records of otters domesticated and trained to fish occurs during the T'ang dynasty in China, 608–916 A.D. Similar records exist of this practice in medieval Europe. Court records indicate that James I of England kept "cormorants, ospreys, and otters for fishing" and paid a keeper to take care of them in 1618. Other reports of otters kept as pets or used as hunting animals come from Sweden, Poland, France, Switzerland, Germany, South America, India, and Malaysia. Otters have long been hunted, a sport particularly popular among the royalty in England, where otter hounds were bred and kept for this purpose. The records of the American Kennel Club indicate the most famous pack of otter hounds in English history was the Hawkstone Pack of Geoffrey Hill, credited with killing 704 otters between 1870 and 1890. Probably the most famous pet otters were those of Gavin Maxwell, as described in his book *Ring of Bright Water*.

Information on the historic numbers and distribution of the river otter in Colorado is limited. Edward Warren, who wrote a major work on the mammals of Colorado in 1942, entitled *The Mammals of Colorado: Their Habits and Distribution*, reported that there had been only a few otter sightings in Colorado (Colorado, Gunnison, Yampa, Platte, and Arkansas rivers). David Armstrong's *Distribution of Mammals in Colorado* (1970), reported practically no museum specimens in the form of old skulls and skins and speculated that the species had never been abundant in the state. Warren suggested that the otter had primarily been confined to the "larger streams where it could find deep water and plenty of fish." It appears that whatever populations were native to Colorado were probably decimated by extensive beaver trapping and by habitat loss from mining and channelization. Otters were susceptible to extirpation because of their low population densities and low reproductive rate. The last otters in Colorado (prior to reintroduction efforts in the 1970s) were killed in either 1906 or 1909, on the Yampa River in what is today Dinosaur National Monument. Undocumented reports persisted long after this.

NATURAL HISTORY

As with most furbearing animals, our knowledge of the river otter was, for many years, limited to that which was necessary to successfully trap or hunt the animal. It was given the Latin name *Mustela lutra canadensis* by Schreber in 1776, and *Lutra canadensis* by Sabine in 1823. In 1795 it was described by Samuel Hearne in his book *Journey to the Northern Ocean*. In 1829, the otter was mentioned in *Fauna Boreali American*, by John Richardson, and the *Quadrupeds of Northern America*, published in 1849 by Audubon and Bachman, also describes the river otter. Merriam discussed the eastern river otter in his book *Mammals of the Adirondacks* (1884). In 1929, Ernest Thompson Seton assembled much of the natural history lore and legends regarding the otter in his book *Lives of Game Animals*. Since then, much research has been conducted into the fascinating ecology of the otter, but much still needs to be learned before we can properly manage wild populations.

The river otter is a member of the genus *Lutra*, which comprises weasel-like animals of medium size with short legs and long tails that are adapted for life in the water. Some of the characteristics of the river otter that help it to live in the water include its body shape, its webbed feet, and its dense oily fur. Otters are piscivores, aquatic carnivorous mammals that prey primarily on fish and compete only with predatory fish in that ecological niche. One of the best physical descriptions of the river otter has been written by the biologist Dale Toweill in Chapman and Feldhammer's *Wild Mammals of North America*:

> In general body conformation, the northern river otter resembles a long cylinder that reaches its greatest diameter in the thoracic region. The head is rather blunt, small, and somewhat flattened. It is characterized by a bulbous nose on the end of a short muzzle, small rounded ears set well back, and eyes set high on the head and closer to the nose than to the ears. The neck is thick and cylindrical. Legs are short and stocky . . . The tail is relatively long, thick, and pointed.

The naturalist Ernest Thompson Seton described the fur color of the river otter as:

> . . . dark, rich, glossy brown, becoming paler and grayer below; the brown of the head and muzzle changes on lips, cheeks, chin, and throat, rather abruptly into a pale brownish gray, almost a gray brown. Some specimens are much paler.

Instances of albinism are reported in otters. Colorado Division of Wildlife wildlife researcher Tom Beck, now in charge of the river otter project in the state, reports to me that otter fur color is quite variable throughout its range, and may even be a function of water chemistry. The fur itself is relatively short but is amazing in its thickness. Sea otter studies, Beck adds, suggest that the fur, and not the underlying layer of fat, is the greatest contributor to insulation. A river otter can swim comfortably in the coldest of waters. These same qualities — a beautiful and warm pelt — are what make it so valued by trappers and by those for whom they trap.

Adult female otters generally are smaller than adult males. Adult weights range from eleven to thirty pounds, with the average around twenty pounds. The overall length of a fully grown otter is normally around forty inches. The tail is usually about one foot in length. The hind feet, averaging about three inches in length, are about one inch longer than the front feet. Biologist Dale Toweill reports that "dentition, while less massive than that of the sea otter (*Enhydra lutra*), is heavy when compared with most other Mustelids. Teeth are adapted for crushing." Seen in profile, the canine teeth of the river otter are quite large, and are well suited for their function of quickly dispatching prey. Jaw musculature is impressive.

When a good population is present, otter sign is not difficult to find. Dave Stevens, Park Biologist at Rocky Mountain National Park, has told me that he can go into the Kawuneeche Valley at just about any time and with only a little effort find some evidence of the otters living there. Otter sign normally found includes the tracks, which show the five digits with their respective claw prints, as well as the central pad and impressions of the webbing; haul-outs, where the otters find it convenient to leave the water; scent posts, where the otters scratch together soil and debris; dig sights, where otters dig in the substrate; and scats, which ordinarily have fish scales and vertebrae in them. Dale Toweill, in his summary account in *Wild Mammals of North America* describes otter denning activity:

Northern river otters do not excavate their own dens, but rather use dens dug by other animals or natural shelters. Audubon (in Coues 1877) described an otter den he examined in the hollow trunk of a large tree; Yeager (1938) described similar dens. Also used are vacated beaver or nutria (*Myocastor coypus*) dens, hollow logs, log jams or drift piles, jumbles of loose rock, abandoned or unused boathouses, and duck blinds. Otters will on occasion build a nestlike structure in aquatic vegetation.

Toweill further notes that otters are most active in the period from dawn to midmorning and during the evening, with the peak of feeding activity from dawn to midmorning.

River otters are believed to breed in late winter or early spring. Copulation may occur either on land or in the water, but, according to Dale Toweill, usually occurs in the water. One description related by Toweill in his account has the otter approaching the female from the rear, holding her by the loose scruff of her neck with his teeth, and bending the posterior part of his body around and below her broad tail as he breeds with her. Toweill notes that:

Receptive female otters may advertise their condition by marking at scent stations or haul-outs. Liers reported that otter hunters sometimes locate such areas and that they may kill two or three males following a female in estrus. He reported that male otters are normally solitary and do not form pair bonds with females, although they may fight to prevent other males from approaching a female in estrus. Home range of a solitary male may overlap that of one or more females.

River otters display delayed implantation, in which the blastocyst, or embryo, is arrested for a period before it is implanted in the uterine wall. This phenomenon is also found in the black and grizzly bear, and is thought to be a strategy developed in relation to hibernation. It is not known what advantages the otter gains from delayed implantation. Toweill reports that the length of gestation may range from 288 to 375 days, with the active period of pregnancy only about fifty days. Parturition may occur from November through May, with the peak period in March or April. The young are born in a den, with litters ranging in size from one to six. Two to four are considered the norm. Males play no role in the raising of the young. Toweill describes the early life of the river otter:

Although helpless at birth, young otters begin to open their eyes by the age of 21 to 35 days, and by 25 to 42 days they begin playing with each other and with their mother. The pups may be introduced to the water by the age of 48 days and may venture out of the den on their own by the age of 59 to 70 days. By 49 days, young begin to use a specific, localized area for defecation. At the age of 63 to 76 days they begin eating solid food, although weaning does not occur until about 91 days.

Otter range in North America is enormous, from the highest mountains to desert rivers, from Arctic rivers to marine areas. Many of these habitats are far from being pristine. Biologist Tom Beck states:

> . . . many seriously polluted rivers support otter and fish—lower Mississippi River, Atchafalanga River basin, Sabine River, east shore (Maryland) of Chesapeake Bay—all are polluted. I'm not in favor of pollution, but someone jumped on pollution in general as a limiting factor of otter and the evidence isn't there to support it.

Biologist Dale Toweill notes that:

> [river otters] are scarce, however, in heavily settled areas, particularly if the waterways are polluted, and in food-poor mountain streams. Mowbray *et al.* (1979) reported that no northern river otter occurred in waters altered by acidic mine drainages in Maryland. Little work has been done in evaluating the range of water quality that otters will tolerate.

Studying the river otter in Colorado will no doubt help us to better understand the relation between pollution—particularly from mining—and river otters.

The bulk of the otter diet is fish, with crustaceans (primarily crayfish), amphibians, insects, birds, and mammals comprising a smaller portion. One reference in the literature cited by Toweill indicates that otters fed in captivity on a basic diet of live fish do poorly. Diversity of diet may be important. Otters seem to select for injured, weakened, and slower-swimming fish. Larger fish may be less maneuverable and hence more vulnerable. In a mountain stream, for example, a sucker might be easier for an otter to capture than a trout, and may thus comprise a larger part of the diet, even though there are fewer suckers than trout in the area.

Otter home ranges vary greatly, depending on quality of habitat, presence

Subalpine riparian habitat on the North Fork of the Colorado River, approximately one mile north of the Lulu City trailhead in Rocky Mountain National Park. This river is now home for several dozen river otters. Thunder Mountain (12,070 feet) is visible in the background. River bed is 9,300 feet. *John Murray*

of man-related disruptions, and other environmental factors. Toweill reports of a study in Sweden:

> There, otters have well-defined home ranges, each containing a number of areas of relatively intensive use — dens, rolling areas, slides, feeding places, sprainting areas (defecation sites), haul-outs, and runways. Family groups consisting of an adult female and her young were found to utilize an area about 7 km in diameter during a year, with the diameter increasing from 3 to 4 km to the full width as the pups mature (Erlinge 1967). Male otters were found to occupy home ranges much more extensive and variable in size than those of females. Home range areas of males averaged about 15 km in width but were highly variable in length . . . Otters maintained territories within their home ranges . . . delineated by marks and signs . . . Direct conflicts were rare.

In his study of river otters on the North Fork of the Colorado River in Rocky Mountain National Park (Kawuneeche Valley), Colorado State

University graduate student Curtis Mack found that most home-range lengths (measured by straight-line waterway distance) were 19.8 miles. Male otters maintained home ranges averaging 27.28 miles in length. Females maintained home ranges averaging 11.3 miles in length. There are a number of theories as to why male river otters have larger home ranges than females. We will see this same dramatic disparity in home-range size as we look at male and female black-footed ferrets and at male and female grizzly bears later in this book. Toweill makes the following observation about river otter home-range size, based on a Swedish study:

> The primary significance of territoriality for family groups involved securing feeding areas, while territoriality in males served to secure a breeding area. Transient otters could pass through maintained territories.

He notes that biologists studying otters in Idaho found "little evidence of territoriality," and concludes that "otter population density is probably an important factor in determining whether territoriality is exhibited."

Otters are well known for their unusual intelligence, which probably accounts in part for their widespread popularity. As Toweill noted:

> They are extremely curious animals and may readily be trained to perform a wide variety of activities, and, of course, their inclination to make a "game" out of almost any activity is almost legendary. Much of their active time is spent exploring new surroundings or objects, often in the form of apparent play. Northern river otters have been taught to retrieve objects from land and water, to capture and retrieve fish, and to hunt other animals . . . The memory of river otters is exceptional.

Otters are extremely social mammals, and enjoy such things as underwater acrobatics, games of tag in the water, ducking contests, and playful wrestling matches. Some observers have reported their use of communal slides on which they slide down steep muddy banks or snow banks for many hours. At these times they communicate with a variety of grunts, growls, chuckles, and cries. Toweill reports that in the bedding of captive otters it is common to find small shells, rounded pebbles, and other natural playthings they bring to the nest to amuse themselves. Otters have great manual dexterity.

Causes of mortality in the wild include predators, malnourishment, parasites, loss of habitat, disease, road kills, hunting, and trapping. Parasites include trematodes, cestodes, and nematodes. Diseases include canine distemper, jaundice, hepatitis, pneumonia, and even human tuberculosis. Natural predators include bobcats, domestic dogs, coyotes, wolves, foxes, alligators, crocodiles, cougars, lynxes, and black and grizzly bears. Humankind has altered or destroyed much of the otter's original habitat in North America, and remains its worst enemy. Many states and provinces still allow the trapping of otters for their pelts. As long as there remains a market for these products, trapping will continue.

CURRENT STATUS AND FUTURE RECOVERY

The Colorado Division of Wildlife first initiated a river otter recovery project in 1972. The Colorado Nongame, Endangered, or Threatened Species Conservation Act of 1973 directed the Division to identify threatened and endangered species within the state and "establish programs for the protection and enhancement of those species." State law also directed the Wildlife Commission, an oversight body appointed by the governor, to "prepare and implement recovery plans for threatened and endangered species which have a high biological potential to become self-sustaining." Subsequently, the Division undertook a statewide search of waters. Prior to reintroduction, the Division had received numerous unconfirmed sightings for the Colorado, Blue, Conejos, and Gunnison rivers, and for Williams Creek Reservoir (Hinsdale County). Other unconfirmed sightings existed for the Arkansas, Platte, Rio Grande, White, and Republican rivers. The last substantiated report had been in 1906 or 1909. It was determined that no self-sustaining populations existed in Colorado. Because of the regulation of water quality and the control of beaver trapping, the Division recognized that there was good potential for reestablishing viable otter populations in Colorado. Additionally, there was significant public interest in a river otter recovery.

A River Otter Recovery Team was soon formed, consisting of representatives from the National Park Service, United States Forest Service, United States Fish and Wildlife Service, and Colorado Division of Wildlife. The objective of the recovery plan, it was decided, would be:

> Establishing two separate self-sustaining populations of river otter (*Lutra canadensis*) in Colorado by 1990. Each population should be composed of a minimum of 50 reproductively active animals with a 50/50 sex ratio.

With the accomplishment of this objective, the team agreed the river otter could be downlisted from Endangered to Threatened, with delisting as the ultimate goal.

River otter shortly after release in Colorado. *Colorado Division of Wildlife*

Because Colorado did not at the time have any resident self-sustaining populations of otters, any recovery effort meant that the otter had to be trapped in an area of high density, transported to Colorado, and released in suitable habitat. Otters originally were obtained from Newfoundland, Washington, Oregon, Wisconsin, Michigan, and Minnesota. Reintroductions initially were made into the North Fork of the Colorado River in Rocky Mountain National Park (thirty-nine otters), the Black Canyon of the Gunnison (twenty-one otters), the Piedra River (twenty-four otters), and Cheesman Reservoir (four otters). Post-release surveys for the Piedra River and Black Canyon populations have been inconclusive with respect to survival, dispersal, and reproduction. It is believed there was one hundred per cent mortality for the Cheesman Reservoir population. The most studied population has been that in Rocky Mountain National Park.

From July 1, 1981 to July 1, 1984, the river otters on the North Fork of the Colorado River (Kawuneeche Valley) in Rocky Mountain National Park were the object of an intense research project by Curtis Mack, a graduate student in the Department of Fishery and Wildlife Biology at Colorado State University. The first release of otters into the Park occurred in 1978, when seven river otters from Wisconsin were reintroduced on the North Fork. A preliminary radiotelemetry program was initiated with seven more Wisconsin river otters released in 1980. This research was expanded in 1981 when Mack began his study. Through the fall of 1983, a total of thirty-nine animals were released into the study area, with twenty-three of them implanted with radio transmitters (maximum life of twenty-four months). Seven more females were reintroduced in 1984. Radio transmitters are surgically implanted into the abdomens of river otters. Because of difficulties with radio-tracking collars slipping off, they are not placed on the neck.

The objectives of Mack's study were to: 1) describe habitats available to otters in the study area; 2) monitor otter response to reintroduction; 3) determine available prey base within the study area; 4) develop an energetics model for adult river otters based on the literature; and 5) from the above, develop an index of release-site suitability. The reintroduction of threatened and endangered species into historic habitat is a relatively new process to science. In the past, reintroduction efforts, whether wolves in Michigan or caribou in Maine, have sometimes failed to establish viable populations because there has been insufficient initial stocking with healthy individuals, inadequate follow-up procedures, and inadequate knowledge of habitat requirements. Mack's study was oriented to help gain a fuller understanding of the subtleties of reintroduction, and acquire useful information that might be beneficial in future efforts.

Mack made a number of significant contributions to our understanding of otter biology, at least as it is found on the North Fork of the Colorado River. Perhaps most importantly, he was unable to document a single case of reproduction for the Kawuneeche population. It is unknown why this is the case, although several hypotheses have been put forward, including the secretiveness of the otter (which makes it difficult to observe), the marginal nature of the habitat, the physical impairment from the radio package, and the demographics of the population. The real cause could be a combination of these. Mack found that the dominant cause (seventy-eight per cent) of transplanted otter mortality was improper trapping and handling of captive otters prior to release. Some otters were severely injured by the steel traps used to capture them, resulting in broken bones and severed toes. Others died or were injured as a result of surgical procedures or inadequate holding facilities. Also, several otters escaped. He made a number of recommendations directed at reducing unnecessary mortality, including the development of inhalation anesthetic procedures and cage modifications.

Through radiotelemetry, it was learned that the river otters were highly active and highly mobile (otters dispersed as far north as the Cache la Poudre River and North Park). Home-range lengths were found to average 19.8 miles. Male otters maintained larger home ranges (27.3 miles of straight-line waterway on average) than the female otters (11.3 miles of straight-line waterway on average). Spring and summer home ranges were much larger than winter home ranges. Valley habitats were greatly preferred over mountain habitats, with otters found along the North Fork, in tributary streams, in irrigation canals and impoundments, in beaver ponds, in lakes, and in private recreational ponds. It appeared that mountain streams were used by otters only as travel corridors and did not support otters for extended periods. Also, areas affected by humans did not appear to restrict otter movements, with otters observed along developed shorelines and crossing highways, dams, and bridges.

The otters in the North Fork country consumed both trout and suckers, with trout comprising eighty-nine per cent and suckers ten per cent of the available prey. Suckers are more vulnerable to otter predation because they are slower and less shelter-seeking. An estimate from fish data and an energetics model indicated that the Kawuneeche Valley could support five adult female river otters. Energy supply-and-demand analysis predicted that the

Subalpine riparian habitat on the East Inlet approximately two miles east of Grand Lake (Rocky Mountain National Park). River otters have been radio-tracked in these deep cold waters. Mount Craig (12,007 feet) is visible in the background; river bed is 8,800 feet. *John Murray*

availability of prey exceeded the requirements of the otters by sixfold on an annual basis. The same data also indicated that winter habitat—the time of reproduction—is extremely marginal.

Mack's study documented that adult river otters can survive in the Kawuneeche Valley. The survival rate was 72.4 per cent for telemetered animals. Mack was, however, unable to document reproduction, a critically important factor in evaluating the suitability of high mountain rivers and streams for otter transplants. It may be that more suitable otter habitat is found elsewhere in the state at lower elevations. In his final recommendations, Mack suggested the following: 1) develop a statewide approach in selection of release sites and establishment of goals and objectives; 2) develop improved release site selection; 3) establish both short- and long-term monitoring programs; 4) standardize all data collections methods; 5) continue to monitor Kawuneeche females, with the emphasis on documenting reproduction; 6) conduct annual winter sign surveys in the Kawuneeche area; 7) initiate a trapper's awareness program in Grand County; and 8) initiate research on minimum viable populations for river otters and island population ecology in the context of river otter reintroductions.

In the spring of 1986, Colorado Division of Wildlife wildlife researcher Tom Beck was assigned the job of researching river otter management programs, and exploring what new directions the programs might take in the future. Beck has indicated that the emphasis of research will be on documenting reproduction. He has shown a strong interest in reintroducing otters to some of the desert river systems of the Western Slope, including the Green, lower Colorado, and Dolores. These areas of the Colorado Plateau region may indeed prove to be as good, if not better, than previous release sites.

The last ten years have seen great strides in the river otter recovery effort in Colorado, but, clearly, much more needs to be done. The goal of establishing two self-sustaining populations still eludes us, but is probably within our reach. In retrospect, the choice of the river otter for reintroduction into Colorado seems wise on the part of the Division of Wildlife. The otter has wide appeal, from school children to grandparents. Only a few groups, such as fishermen and waterfowl hunters were affected negatively by the otter restoration, and they only moderately. It was a good place to start, a good way of familiarizing people with the idea of bringing extirpated animals back into the state, particularly since we have the habitat and social acceptance. The river otter restoration effort offers hope and promise for the other endangered mammals in this book, particularly, in the immediate future, the wolverine and lynx.

Few people will ever see the elusive river otters that have been restored to Colorado. *Colorado Division of Wildlife*

To me the otter is emblematic of the water, and particularly symbolic of rivers. The name "otter" in English comes from the ancient Greek *hydor*, meaning water. The two seem inextricably intertwined, almost synonymous — each evokes the other. To have the otters back in this state's waters is as important a statement of philosophy as it is of biology. We are saying that we have made a commitment to keeping our rivers wild. Long ago, from the Nile to the Ganges, people worshipped such things as rivers, and made offerings to them, praying for rain in time of drought and for relief during flood. Those days are gone, but rivers still inspire our awe and wonder. As T.S. Eliot wrote in "The Dry Salvages":

> I do not know much about gods; but I think the river
> Is a strong, brown god — sullen, untamed, and intractable
> •••••
> Keeping his seasons and rages, destroyer, reminder
> Of what men choose to forget . . .

The otter reminds us of the importance of water in a water-scarce state like Colorado, and in a sense is our modern version of that ancient offering. There may be other rivers elsewhere in the universe—we have already seen the alluvial valleys and dendritic canyons of Mars, where rivers flowed long ago. There will be other worlds, other places for the human race to visit long after we are gone. Perhaps there will be other rivers. But there is only one Earth, only one planet with rivers that provide a home for a lovely animal we call the otter. Perhaps our posterity will return to this world, tired from their travels in the cold lonely gulfs between the stars, and will sit down beside the rivers and wait for the otter. They will be thankful that people in our distant age kept them from slipping away downstream.

IV

PRAIRIE HILLS

THE BLACK-FOOTED

FERRET

One of the major variables in the ferret conservation program is its organization and management . . . Whatever review of the ferret program ensues, if any, it should fully review all the major variables so that we can learn the lessons for effective endangered species management in the future. There is too much at stake not to reflect on the ferret program and learn its hard lessons.
— Dr. Tim Clark, *Endangered Species Technical Bulletin* (May, 1986)

INTRODUCTION

A rangy limestone gray coyote looked at me out of the corner of its yellow eye, instinctively lowered its silhouette to the ground, and quickly disappeared into the rolling prairie. I went over to its daybed, actually an old deer bed hollowed out in the soft debris beneath a solitary juniper, and felt where it was still warm. There were downy earth brown feathers on a low branch, left by a burrowing owl, and mice bones in the owl scats nearby. I moved on down the ridge, about as alone as a person can be in Colorado, with the broken white clouds and the fast shadows that scudded behind them slipping over the gentle grass-covered terrain. A chinook was blowing in strong from the west, where the mountains were still covered with snow.

It was a good day to be out on the High Plains, out among the long contours and winding valleys and ancient watercourses. I was out looking not for black-footed ferrets, for they were all gone in northeastern Colorado, but for the wild undisturbed prairie dog colonies in which they had once lived. I had driven east of Boulder until the Front Range radio station had faded into static and had been replaced by a weak signal coming from Wichita. I wanted to get a sense of what the ferret's habitat had been like before grazing and cultivation. I wanted to be out among the unfenced hills, the native grasslands where the buffalo and the wolf, the prairie dog and the ferret, the Indian and the Earth, had all once lived in a natural community that in this age seems incomprehensible. I drove until the obscure country blacktop ended and the unpaved road began, and I followed that until I could go no farther. My map showed it was government land, leased occasionally to the last of the shortgrass ranchers. My instincts told me I had finally found one of the last wild corners of the prairie, a place of tumbleweeds and tornadoes, blizzards and droughts, dreams and nightmares: the hard miserly land of Willa Cather and John Steinbeck and Woody Guthrie.

I topped the low ridge, crossed a wide valley, climbed in and out of a deep arroyo, and picked up an old road base that seemed to twist and turn to nowhere in particular. After a mile or so, I reached an unkempt field enclosed by a high chain-link fence topped with rolls of barbed wire. Several large concrete bunkers could be seen looming inside, of the sort used to house our euphemistic nemesis, the Minuteman. The whole compound, probably once kept carefully mowed and policed, was now overgrown with sunflowers, prickly pear cactus, wild poppies, and Canadian thistle. A bullet-ridden, sandblasted, half-demolished sign hung sideways from the creaking gate by one last twist of insulated copper wire, which looked like it hadn't been opened in years. The first morning glory tendrils had begun to cover it: "Aviso! Warning! Restricted Area! Use of Deadly Force Authorized! United States Air Force Missile Facility! Unlawful To Enter Without Permission of Base Commander! (Section 21, Internal Security Act 1950, 50 USC 797) Property of the United States Government." The only base commander visible now was a yellow-throated western meadowlark, perched on top of the rusting screw to an abandoned manhole cover, insistently warning off all intruders with his proud, melodic song. I pressed on.

When I reached the top of the next ridge, which offered a good view of the whole country, I saw my first prairie dog village. It was built on an alluvial outwash bench in the next valley, a bustling metropolis established on a perfectly flat piece of real estate, dotted as regularly as a subdivision with small excavated mounds. There were perhaps fifty or sixty burrows in the town, not much compared to the huge colonies that once stretched as large as whole counties over the plains. The village was just south of a small copse of weathered cottonwood and alder, the sort the Indians used to camp under as they followed the herds of bison, elk, antelope, and deer, and the kind of place a wagon master might pull his Conestogas into after a long hard day on the trail. It looked like there was a small stream running in the dead cattails on the far side of the village. A lone willow had already started to bud. Beyond it was a small broken ridge topped with juniper and pinyon.

I stretched out, laying flat on the gramma grass with my chin resting on my folded arms, and began to study the hustle and bustle of the colony. My perspective was approximately that of a black-footed ferret, just a few inches above the sun-cured grass, crawling ants, cast-off .22–250 shells, and scattered droppings of pronghorn antelope and jackrabbit. He comes over a ridge like this, I thought, late in the day, leaving one valley for a new valley, and then he sees it, off in the distance, with a gleam in his eye. Perhaps he waits here, patiently, until after the sun has gone down and the color has faded from the west and the last bird's beak has closed, and then he stalks in from sage to sage beneath a rising bull-horn moon and the twinkling Pleiades. Creeping slowly and silently he closes in, with nothing but the worst intentions for the peacefully sleeping, law-abiding residents of Prairie-Dogville.

After a while I removed my old 7 × 35 binoculars from their case and focused upon a sage-rimmed stage of high and low drama, with well over a hundred different strutting and fretting personalities. These were *Cynomys ludovicianus*, the black-tailed prairie dog, once the staple food of the local ferrets. These dogs were plump, short-legged, and tawny in color, with a shape reminiscent of the guinea pigs that children fatten and breed. They certainly did not resemble any dog that I have ever seen. Their tails were short and perky, and jerked expressively as they moved. They moved in a gait best described as a scurry. The whole town was full of dog talk, a diverse cacophony consisting of squeaks, squeals, barks, chatters, clucks, and chuckles. A ferret could listen to this sound and know its source. For most of their lives, ferrets actually live in prairie dog towns, much to the displeasure of the residents.

When two prairie dogs meet they greet each other like Russian diplomats with a crude form of kiss, barely touching their bared teeth together. Once certain of each other, their tails stop flicking and each begins to groom the other, nibbling, pawing, nuzzling, pecking, probing, even offering their most private regions for inspection. Part of this ritual is psychological, to

Black-footed ferret habitat in Eastern Colorado. *William Ervin*

reinforce the social bonds necessary for so many animals to occupy so small a place. Another part is hygienic, to remove the annoying fleas that bedevil the dogs and occasionally carry a plague that decimates whole colonies.

About half the population were engaged in this grooming activity. The other half were either nursing young pups, in the process of reexcavating and building burrows damaged during the winter, or out foraging at the edges of the known world. These last were the most fearful and nervous animals, and regularly stood up on their hind feet to look around. A handful of grizzled dogs back at the colony appeared to be lookouts, and were constantly surveying all points of the compass and of the sky. These also seemed to be the biggest dogs, the two- or three-pounders that can actually kill or seriously wound a ferret in single combat. These are no doubt the brave sort of dogs that run over and try to cover up a hole as soon as a ferret (or worse, a rattlesnake) enters it.

We now know that these rodents are an integral part of the ecology and health of the prairie. They reprocess and revitalize the compacted earth with their burrowing. They create loam where there was only silt and clay, and fertilize it with their droppings and their bodies and their granaries.

They attract and nurture other forms of life, providing a haven for the spider and the snake, the bird and the mammal, communally supporting an intricate web of prairie life. Perhaps most important, they are excellent converters of green stuff—chlorophyll—into red stuff—meat. Protein. The sustenance of any carnivore, from owls to bobcats to red foxes to coyotes.

Suddenly a shrill, high-pitched warning chirp was sounded. Pandemonium. One hundred dogs scurrying for their holes. Imminent disaster. No time for the meek. Death is everywhere. Dog alert! Dog alert! Dogs rudely pushing aside dogs as they clamor for the safety of their subterranean bunkers. In the time it takes to read this description, the village stood empty. One wizened head rose up briefly, and then vanished. From the northwest, a red-tailed hawk was making his final approach, hoping perhaps to surprise a fat dog far outside the perimeter, forgetful of all caution as he foraged greedily for early spring morsels. But none were to be found outside the thin red line. The raptor's wide shadow passed silently over the vacant craters like that of an enemy warplane over a battlefield. The bird flew on, with a defiant, downslurred *kee ahrrr!* soaring out over the prairie in search of

The prairie dog is as important to the black-footed ferret as the snowshoe hare is to the lynx. *Colorado Division of Wildlife*

other prey. One by one the heads looked up and the little brown dogs scurried forth. When all were out in the sun once again, a triumphant chorus of dog cheers arose, echoing across the emptiness. I decided, as I turned to leave, that there was life, society, and humor here. The prairie dogs deserved to live. They had a purpose under the sun. And so did the black-footed ferret. They were pests only in the narrowest and most uninformed sense.

His name comes from the Latin *furittus*, meaning little thief, and he is the one I most missed by the end of the day. His absence was conspicuous. I longed to see the supple minklike body gliding among the burrows, the striking black robber's mask, like that of a raccoon, the large round ears pressed intently forward, the bright buttonlike eyes. A ferret would be fun to watch, near dusk, when it comes up out of its burrow and yawns and stretches and scratches and looks around at the grasslands. Unfortunately, because of its intimate predator-prey association with the prairie dog, the fate of the ferret has been closely linked to that of the prairie dog. The combination of habitat loss due to grazing and cultivation coupled with a program of active poisoning has proved devastating for the ferret. It is estimated that the prairie dog inhabited about 700 million acres in the West in the late 1800s. By 1971 that original habitat had shrunk to less than 1.5 million acres. Today the black-footed ferret is one of the most critically endangered mammals in the world. There may be less than two dozen left. By the time the first edition of this book goes out of print, the black-footed ferret may be extinct.

PAST HISTORY

Ferrets are believed to have evolved in Asia and then crossed over to the New World by the Bering Land Bridge, advancing southeastward to the Great Plains via available ice-free corridors. Prairie dog remains have been found in at least six of the Pleistocene sites in which ferret remains were located. The closest relatives of the black-footed ferret are the European (domestic) polecat, and the Steppe ferret, also known as the Siberian polecat. The Siberian polecat inhabits the steppe and forested steppe zones of Eurasia and preys on ground-dwelling sciurids (squirrel-like animals), such as the gerbil. Fossil remains of the Siberian polecat have been found in late Pleistocene sites in Alaska. It is believed that it is the ancestor of the black-footed ferret. Whether the black-footed ferret and the Siberian polecat are of the same or different species is an important genetic question that has yet to be resolved. In general appearance, the two are almost identical. Cranial measurements show no significant differences, and further suggest the two may be conspecific (genetically compatible). The earliest fossil record of the black-footed ferret is from an Upper Illinoian deposit in Clay County, Nebraska. Other ferret remains have been found in Alaska, the Yukon, Alberta, Montana, Idaho, Wyoming, Colorado, New Mexico, and Texas. It is obvious from these fossilized remains that the black-footed ferret and the prairie dog have lived in close association for many thousands of years.

Prior to European settlement and American expansion, the Plains Indians held the black-footed ferret in particularly high regard, using the pelts as talismans in certain religious ceremonies, as well as to adorn the headdresses of their chiefs. Stuffed black-footed ferrets, sometimes decorated with colored cloth bands and feathers, have been found as Indian relics in both Wyoming and Montana. Their use by the Indians for these special purposes suggests to some that either the black-footed ferret has always been scarce, or that the species was difficult, even among the Indians, to obtain.

The original range of the black-footed ferret was approximately the same as that of the three species of prairie dog—black-tailed prairie dog, white-tailed prairie dog, and Gunnison's prairie dog—upon which it depends for food. The black-footed ferret extended over the entire Great Plains from southern Canada to the west Texas plains, and from east of the hundredth meridian into Montana, Wyoming, Utah, Colorado, and Arizona. It is generally acknowledged that various land-use practices, particularly cultivation and predator and rodent poisoning campaigns, have resulted in the decline of prairie dog habitat to only .07 of previous range, and the consequent decline of the black-footed ferret.

The war against the prairie dog began as early as 1880 in some areas, intensified in the early 1900s as state governments joined the campaign, and reached its zenith in the period from 1916–1972, when the federal government contributed greatly to the effort. Before 1944, popular poisons included strychnine, thallium sulphate, and cyanide. To kill rodents, the poisons were placed on grain, which was then distributed at prairie dog burrows. Predators were killed when the poison was either placed inside or injected into a fifty- or one hundred-pound piece of meat, and then staked out in the open. After June, 1944, Compound 1080 (sodium monofluoroacetate), an odorless, tasteless white salt, was widely used. The poison was considered more effective than the other three compounds. It is chemically stable in body tissue and can kill predators that feed on poisoned animals. It is possi-

The most distinctive aspect of the black-footed ferret's head is the black robber's mask. *Tim Clark*

ble that ferrets were poisoned by Compound 1080 before it was generally banned in 1972.

Currently, the only black-footed ferret population known positively to exist is that on the upper Greybull River in northwestern Wyoming near the town of Meeteetse. It probably numbers fewer than twelve right now (according to the U.S. Fish and Wildlife Service and BIOTA), although the Wyoming Game and Fish Department estimates twenty. Small scattered black-footed ferret populations may still exist in the former range, including several locations in Colorado, but these populations remain unverified by biologists. Because of their insular status, breeding opportunities at these locations are probably insufficient to maintain their numbers.

The black-footed ferret was first described by John James Audubon and John Bachman in 1851 after studying a skin brought to them from Wyoming. They classified it as *Mustela nigripes*, or the black-footed member of the mustelids, a large musk-producing family that includes skunk, otter, weasel, mink, marten, wolverine, and badger. Another specimen was not reported again for twenty-five years, during which time many experts doubted the ferret's existence. For nearly one hundred years after the Audubon-Bachman report, the black-footed ferret was rarely if ever observed in the wild, and little was known of its habits or habitat.

During the early 1950s, the U.S. government began to collect and organize data on the distribution of the black-footed ferret. Officials were dismayed to learn that the ferret was even more scarce than formerly believed, and that only one small area in South Dakota appeared to have any signs of regular ferret activity. Proposals were made to study the ferret, and even to livetrap and release them in protected prairie dog towns in national parks, but only one abortive attempt was made. In an age when most people were more concerned with the atomic bomb, the war in Korea, civil rights, McCarthyism, and other pressing social issues, there was little interest in an obscure animal of the Great Plains that seemed to enjoy living among prairie dogs. This was also a period of low environmental awareness. There was widespread belief in private and in public sectors that the proper way to treat predators and rodents was to destroy them with poison. The extermination policies of the federal and state governments at this time were not so much malicious as they were ignorant. Had they known what we know now, they probably would have ceased or greatly reduced their destruction of prairie dog colonies and the historic predators of the plains.

For many years, the South Dakota population (concentrated in a five-county region in the southcentral part of the state) was thought to be the last group of black-footed ferrets in the world. In 1953, Walt Disney procured several ferrets from trappers for a movie called *The Vanishing Prairie*. Ironically, one of these ferrets died in a trap and another died of a previous gunshot wound during the filming. The others survived the movie and were turned over to the superintendent of Wind Cave National Park in southwestern South Dakota, where they were released and never seen again. In 1960 there were nine sightings in South Dakota (four dead). In 1961 there were two, in 1962 there were five, and in 1963 eight live ferrets and four dead ferrets were observed. The black-footed ferret was one of the first species to be placed on the U.S. Endangered Species list in 1966. The South Dakota population was studied from 1964 until 1974, when the population apparently disappeared. Since 1974 there have been a number of black-footed ferret sightings in this region, including several by credible sources, but there has been no verification. The last of the captive black-footed ferrets removed from this area died at the U.S. Fish and Wildlife Service Laboratory at Patuxent, Maryland in 1979, at the advanced age of twelve or thirteen years, after having given birth to several litters of stillborn pups.

After a ferret was discovered drowned in a stock tank in Carbon County, Wyoming in 1972, efforts were made to determine if a second population existed in southern Wyoming. From 1972 to 1979, a total of fifty-seven probable and confirmed black-footed ferret sightings were made in this area. On September 25, 1981, a black-footed ferret (adult male) was killed by Lucille and John Hogg's dog on a ranch near Meeteetse. After being turned over to a taxidermist, the body was identified as a black-footed ferret and local and federal wildlife officials were called in. A meeting was called of the local ranchers and townspeople, and it was soon learned that an employee of a local ranch had recently seen a black-footed ferret at another location. In a quick search of the area, fresh ferret tracks in the snow, two ferretlike trenches, and a single scat were located, indicating that a ferret probably was in the region. On October 29, 1981, at about 6:20 A.M., U.S. Fish and Wildlife Service employees searching the ranch observed a live black-footed ferret in a prairie dog town. It was live-captured eleven hours later, and, after a brief examination, released back into the wild with a radio collar. The scientific community was elated, and conservationists were ecstatic at the discovery of a second population of black-footed ferrets.

Shortly after this, Tim Clark, head of BIOTA Research and Consulting and a research associate at Idaho State University, and employees from the Denver Wildlife Research Center of the U.S. Fish and Wildlife Service began intensive prairie dog and ferret surveys in the Meeteetse area. This

Black-footed ferrets are best spotlighted in the summer months, when they are actively hunting during the cool night hours. *Tim Clark*

was to become a four-year study of the black-footed ferrets and of the local colonies of white-tailed prairie dogs. Max Schroeder headed the DWRC effort in 1981 and 1982, before becoming the Black-Footed Ferret Recovery Team Coordinator. Kathleen A. Fagerstone and Dean Biggins headed the program from 1983 to 1985. The study included snowtracking and spotlighting surveys, telemetry studies, prairie dog studies, small mammal studies, and plague monitoring. It was a cooperative effort of state, federal, and private individuals and produced much of the data scientists now have on the ecology of the black-footed ferret. It initially gave hope to those who had written the original U.S. Fish and Wildlife Service Black-Footed Ferret Recovery Plan in June 1978 that at last a sizable and stable population had been found from which ferrets could be removed, bred in captivity, and then transplanted around their historic range.

For three years (1981–1984), everything went well with the research program. At one point U.S. Fish and Wildlife Service biologists were monitoring eleven radio-collared ferrets, as well as a coyote, six badgers, two great horned owls, and two raccoons (to learn more about interspecies relationships). Spotlighting and snowtracking also were used to map and study the black-footed ferret population. It was during this period that a disagreement developed between Wyoming Game and Fish officials and representatives of the federal effort as to whether or not some ferrets should be removed from the wild and placed in a captive breeding program. At that time, there appeared to be enough ferrets to justify this protective move, but Wyoming officials believed the population should be left intact in Wyoming to the greatest extent possible, and their view prevailed. This decision was to have fatal results.

The first hint that something was wrong was in September 1984, when George Menkens, a graduate student at the University of Wyoming trapping prairie dogs in a Meeteetse colony, reported a decline in prairie dog numbers. Later Dave Belitsky, the black-footed ferret coordinator for the Wyoming Game and Fish Department, found the same situation. Biologists immediately suspected that sylvatic plague, a highly infectious bacterium carried by fleas, had infected the colony. In June 1985, after testing by Sonya Ubico, a graduate student at Colorado State University working for the U.S. Fish and Wildlife Service, it was confirmed: fleas taken from five of seven sample locations tested positively for sylvatic plague (known as bubonic, pneumonic, or septicemic plague in humans). An emergency plague-eradication project was implemented, using an insecticide in dust form spread over 6,200 acres of critical black-footed ferret habitat.

Researchers quickly mobilized their resources to determine what effect this massive loss of prey was having on the ferret population, who rely very little on alternative prey species in the area. The results were alarming. In 1984 the spotlight count had been 129. Spotlighters in July and August of 1985 were able to find only 58 ferrets (thirteen litters), as compared to 129 ferrets (twenty-five litters) at the same time in 1984. Many of these ferrets were seen only once, unlike observations in past years where ferrets, once located, could be found night after night. Mark/recapture population estimates showed only thirty-one, plus or minus eight ferrets, about September 10; sixteen, plus or minus eight ferrets, about October 9; and six about November 1, 1985. A loss of about 150 ferrets can be documented between fall 1984 and fall 1985. During July through September, ferrets were dying at the rate of about one every two to three days. In other words, the population was being reduced by about fifty per cent every thirty days. The worst news was the decline in the number of juveniles, essential for the survival of the species.

The probable cause was later diagnosed as canine distemper, always present in nature, and probably brought in by skunks, raccoons, foxes, or coyotes. It is thought unlikely that the canine distemper was brought into the area by researchers. After realizing the severity of the situation, state and federal managers immediately authorized an emergency capture program to remove the ferrets to safety. Between September 12 and October 11, 1985, six ferrets were live-captured from Meeteetse and placed in a Wyoming Game and Fish facility. On October 22, canine distemper was diagnosed when one of the captive ferrets died and another showed symptoms of the disease. Unfortunately, all six ferrets were housed in the same room. Because distemper can spread through the air, all died. Another six ferrets were caught between October 25 and November 1. These were housed individually at Laramie. All six still live. Four are adult females and two are juvenile males. Four of these may be related as mother/offspring and siblings.

The combination of the plague infestation among the prairie dogs and the outbreak of canine distemper in the ferret populations proved devastating for the black-footed ferrets of Meeteetse. While the loss of habitat because of prairie dog mortality probably reduced ferret numbers between July 1984 and July 1985 (one area lost had been very productive for ferret litters), the coup de grace was administered by the canine distemper outbreak. Had some ferrets been livetrapped in 1983 and 1984 (as several researchers suggested), and placed in a captive breeding program, the situation for the ferret might not be so grim today. It was known that the ferrets of Meeteetse annually experienced losses of about sixty-seven per cent of the total population (juveniles eighty-five per cent, adults fifty per cent). Predation from owls, hawks, eagles, coyotes, and badgers, and losses from accidents and dispersal seemed to account for this huge annual ferret mortality. This meant that a "surplus" of Meeteetse ferrets existed for captive breeding. A few of the ferrets that would be lost to natural causes each winter could be removed for captive rearing programs. Additionally, researchers warned that this population, like the one in South Dakota in the 1960s and 1970s, was vulnerable to epidemic diseases and sudden, unpredictable collapse. Tragically, the future of the species has been cast in grave doubt.

NATURAL HISTORY

Little has been known about the ecology of the black-footed ferret until recent times. In 1896, when Dr. Clinton Hart Merriam of the Bureau of Biological Survey tried to describe the ferret, he could find only a half-dozen specimens in museums. In 1929, naturalist Ernest Thompson Seton found so few records on the ferret that he concluded the animal had always been rare (a once widespread belief now disputed by some scientists), and that its numbers were probably waning (which was correct). He predicted that the range of the ferret would be found to be the same as that of the prairie dog "unless we succeed in exterminating both species before sufficient notes can be made." He described the black-footed ferret as a "robber baron securely established in the village of his helpless peasantry," noting that "its mating habits, call notes, love notes, song and amusement are wholly unknown." He concluded with a statement far ahead of his time: "with the passing of the Prairie-dog, the ferret, too, will pass."

During the 1940s, the paucity of scientific knowledge about the ferret began to concern biologists. The problem was officially discussed as early as 1952, after which Dr. Victor H. Cahalane, a researcher with the National Park Service, undertook a substantial field survey of the ferret's range. Cahalane collected reports of sixty ferrets seen primarily between 1948 and 1952. These sightings covered ten western states, in a vast area that stretched from northern Montana south into New Mexico and Texas. The only cluster of reports—sixteen in total—came from a five-county region in southcentral South Dakota. Experts shortly concluded that this area was the heart of the ferret's remaining habitat. During the period of 1960 to 1963, several more reports were made in this location. From 1964 to 1974, when the South Dakota population declined and eventually disappeared, a number of studies were made on the ferrets that gave science valued insight into the natural history of the animal. After the discovery of the previously unknown population near Meeteetse in 1981, studies were conducted, and continue to be performed, by scientists with the U.S. Fish and Wildlife Service, the Wyoming Game and Fish Department, and a private contractor, BIOTA. As a result of the studies in South Dakota and Wyoming, much more is known about the ferret than was known in 1966, when the animal was first listed as an endangered species. Much more needs to be learned if the animal survives.

The black-footed ferret is about the size of a mink, but is more slender and weasel-like in appearance. Its long, smooth, tubular body is ideally suited for hunting in the burrows of its primary prey, the prairie dog. Its total length at maturity ranges from eighteen to twenty-four inches, with a tail length of four to six inches, and a weight of 1.5 to 3 pounds. Sexual dimorphism is generally found, with grown females weighing ten per cent less than grown males. The backs and sides of both sexes are buff yellow, with a darker saddle-shaped patch over the back. The under parts are a shade of white. The feet, legs, and the tip of the tail are black. The most distinctive aspect of the ferret, in most sightings, is the black eye mask. The coat does not turn white in the winter. Compared with its two relatives, the Siberian polecat and the European polecat (domestic ferret), the black-footed ferret has a blunter muzzle, less conspicuous guard hairs, and a uniformly cylindrical tail throughout its length, with only the terminal third black. The skull of the black-footed ferret is more massive than that of the weasel or even the mink. The black-footed ferret is relatively long lived, with some individuals in captivity living to twelve or thirteen years. In the wild, however, the life span is probably only three to five years.

Historically, the range of the black-footed ferret spread through the whole of the middle of the North American continent and was coextensive with that of the prairie dog. Habitats included shortgrass prairie, semidesert, and intermontane parks. Specimens have been collected from over 120 of the 500 counties within the historic range of the prairie dog, representing Arizona, New Mexico, Texas, Oklahoma, Colorado, Kansas, Utah, Nebraska, South Dakota, North Dakota, Montana, and Wyoming. Specimens have also been found in Alberta and Saskatchewan. Of the nearly three hundred specimens presently in museums, no more than five were collected at any distance from prairie dog colonies. Authorities estimate that over 700 million acres of western range were occupied by prairie dogs in the late 1800s. Many of these areas provided habitat for the black-footed ferret. Both Warren and Armstrong discussed the former range of the black-footed ferret in Colorado, with Armstrong reporting specimens from thirty-six of the sixty-three counties in the state. Warren mentioned a sighting he made north of Colorado Springs in a prairie dog town in 1942. Armstrong also makes reference to more recent sightings (1952–1972) on the eastern plains and in the southwestern part of the state, as well as to specimens captured in the vicinity of Craig in 1941 and 1942. Both agree the former distribution of the ferret was probably statewide in all suitable habitat, and that the ferret was, at the time of their writing, endangered.

Positive identification of ferret activity is difficult during all seasons of the year, because the animals are largely nocturnal, elusive, and few in number. Even characteristic ferret sign may be inconclusive. One of the most effective search techniques employed by researchers from July through October is spotlighting prairie dog towns at night. When reflected in the spotlight, the eyes of ferrets appear green in color. Although this green is also typical of most other mustelids (and pronghorn antelope) observers with experience can use differences such as eye size, interorbital distances, and behavior to determine species. The second favored technique from December through March is to search by helicopter or on foot for ferret tracks and dirt diggings characteristic of ferret activity. Ferrets excavate soil from within prairie dog burrows, and then deposit it in unique configurations. Mounds are formed when soil is drawn from burrows and heaped into piles, and troughs, either single or multilobed, are formed when ferrets move backward, dragging soil with their front paws.

Ferret tracks, which are virtually indistinguishable from mink tracks, are most readily identifiable in the winter after a fresh snow. Tracks average 1.2 inches wide and 2.3 inches long in Wyoming. Ferrets make the typical mustelid "twin print" track pattern. Each pattern typically measures around 2.3 inches wide and 3.3 inches long. Stride lengths between twin prints average 18.9 inches. Mink tracks are typically found near streams, ponds, or stock tanks in ferret habitats. In these locations, ferret tracks can only be confirmed when characteristic diggings are found in close association with the tracks.

Ferret scats are rarely found. They are typically long and thin, either linear or folded back on themselves, and generally tapered at both ends. Scats are generally black and contain animal hair, particularly yellow prairie dog fur, with occasional bone fragments and, rarely, plant material. Dimensions of unfolded scats average 2.28 inches in length and folded scats average 1.65 inches in length. Ferret skulls are rarely found, but do provide evidence of past ferret presence. Other sign includes hole plugging by prairie dogs and a dual-puncture-hole pattern at the back of prairie dog skulls, indicating mustelid predation.

Ferrets have not been observed mating in the wild, but captive black-footed ferrets have been observed breeding in March and early April. Further evidence that this is the natural breeding period comes from winter snowtracking, which shows significant increases in individual movements in March and early April. Time of birth is also unknown, but is believed to occur in May and early June, after a gestation period of forty-two to forty-five days (as observed in captive ferrets), with litter sizes ranging between three and five. Eleven Wyoming ferret litters first appeared above ground between July 7 and July 29, after the young had resided about forty-five days below ground. Juvenile ferrets seen at this time appeared to be from two-thirds to three-quarters grown. In Wyoming, the ferret families remained together until late August, when the juveniles were frequently separated from each other in different burrows. Gradually the young grew more and more independent, until they appeared to be completely self sustaining by mid-September.

Ferrets may be active throughout the night, and during the summer and fall months at irregular periods during daylight hours. Ferrets can only be seen with any regularity when a female and her young are present. Ferrets are probably less active in the winter, and are probably solitary, except during the breeding season in the early spring and during the summer when the female is raising the young of the year.

Males and females apparently have different-sized home ranges, which are related to their different spatial strategies. Male home ranges are apparently two times the size of females'. Males attempt to gain access to females first and to food second. Females attempt to increase access to food for rearing young. Probably the areas used by females most closely approximate the amount of real space needed by an individual adult ferret to meet its physiological needs. Home range is also affected by prairie dog density, colony size, and colony distribution. In one study in Wyoming, a female used 39.5 acres and a male used 55.3 acres. It is not known how far black-footed ferrets can travel across areas not occupied by prairie dogs, but there is probably a limit based on their behavioral and physiological tolerances to extended travel. One study suggested that a single black-footed ferret would require between sixteen and twenty-four acres of quality habitat to survive.

Predation by ferrets does not significantly reduce prairie dog populations because prairie dogs are typically prolific, and because the ferret eats only what it needs. Ferrets will eat not only prairie dogs (probably ninety per cent of total diet), but also such small mammals as ground squirrels, deer mice, birds, and cottontail rabbits. One estimate determined that a single black-footed ferret would eat approximately twenty prairie dogs between December and March, and that the ferret would be able to extract its winter requirement of food from 1 to 3.5 acres of quality habitat. One of the most important things to ferret survival is the stability of the prey population. The sudden catastrophic decline or collapse of the prey base, such as happened in some prairie dog colonies at Meeteetse with the sylvatic plague epidemic, can be equally devastating to the ferret.

In the wild, ferrets are susceptible to a variety of predators, including domestic dogs and cats, coyotes, eagles, owls, foxes, badgers, bobcats, and ferruginous hawks. Other causes of mortality include parasites, diseases (including canine distemper, to which they are highly vulnerable), and injuries inflicted while hunting prairie dogs, which are formidable prey. Human beings are by far the worst enemy of the black-footed ferret, killing ferrets by poisoning their prey base, destroying their habitat, setting out poisoned bait for other predators that the ferret consumes, hitting them on roads with cars and trucks, and trapping them accidentally or maliciously.

CURRENT STATUS AND FUTURE RECOVERY

Unfortunately, in discussing the current status of the black-footed ferret, a book may not be the most useful means of providing an up-to-date report. The situation is fluid and changes seasonally or more often. The last population estimate, made in October 1985, indicated perhaps 16 black-footed ferrets, only a fraction of the high, 129, counted in 1984. Snow conditions during the winter of 1985–1986 were not conducive for aerial reconaissance, but researchers met with some success during the summer of 1986, counting eleven ferrets. This census included two females with litters of young, and one adult male. As of August 1986, the male has been trapped and plans are in effect to trap the two females and their litters. Six healthy ferrets remain in captivity from previous trapping efforts. It is thought this group, which includes two juvenile males and four females, may be related to one another. None of the females became pregnant in the spring of 1986.

The Captive Breeding Specialists Group (CBSG) of the International Union for the Conservation of Nature and Natural Resources (IUCN) is now advising state and federal scientists in Wyoming on the six captive ferrets. Chaired by Ulysses Seal, the CBSG includes Jim Doherty of the New York Zoological Society and Mike DonCarlos of the Minnesota Zoological Garden, both experts in the care of mustelids in captivity. This group has met several times since December 1985 and has contributed significantly to captive breeding efforts by reviewing facilities, resources, personnel, support, and plans. Their initial studies have concluded that at least twenty ferrets are necessary to found a viable captive population capable of retaining genetic diversity. The CBSG estimated that the two immature males had only a ten per cent chance of breeding successfully in 1986, an estimate that proved accurate. The CBSG also recommended that if fewer than ten ferrets were found in field surveys at Meeteetse during the summer of 1986, they should all be captured and added to the Wyoming Game and Fish captive breeding facility. Perhaps partly because of their influence, the decision has been made to trap all known surviving ferrets at Meeteetse.

Because the fate of the wild Meeteetse ferrets is uncertain over the next decade, and the small captive population's probability of breeding is unknown, it is clear that more ferrets must be found elsewhere to enhance species recovery efforts. In fact, credible reports continue to come in to conservationists of black-footed ferret sightings in other locations. There were eleven reports of ferrets in Colorado between 1981 and 1984, with ten of these in Moffat County. Dinosaur National Monument has had several of these

A black-footed ferret near a prairie dog hole. *Tim Clark*

sightings. Aerial searches by the Colorado Division of Wildlife in both Moffat County and Rio Blanco County during the winter of 1985–1986, looking primarily for the distinctive diggings made by ferrets, met with no success. Tim Clark has led several unsuccessful expeditions into the area. Another location in Colorado also has received some attention. Recently, a biologist radio-monitoring an instrumented eagle near Trinidad discovered the mandible of a ferret in the eagle's nest. This could be the mandible of a domestic ferret or of a black-footed ferret. Because of similarities in dentition, a positive identification has not been made. The Division of Wildlife undertook a survey of the prairie dog colonies known to have been hunted by the eagle, but no ferrets have yet been found.

Sightings have been reported elsewhere in the West, including South Dakota, Utah, Wyoming, Montana, and New Mexico. In some of these states extensive mapping and surveying of prairie dog colonies have also been undertaken in the past, or are contemplated in the future. In Montana, eight major prairie dog colony complexes capable of supporting ferrets have been located. These total about 34,000 acres in 180 colonies. Some of the complexes are larger than Meeteetse, which had about thirty-seven white-tailed prairie dog colonies totaling about eight thousand acres in one hundred square miles. Other Montana complexes are smaller. The Montana prairie dog colonies appear capable of supporting translocated ferrets, and offer dense and abundant prey, small intercolony distances, dense burrow openings, and a dispersed pattern of prey populations. The latter can provide protection from catastrophic disease such as ravaged the isolated Meeteetse population in 1985.

The future of the ferret is, at best, problematic. Like all species, ferrets are susceptible to extinction from both systematic pressures (regular and predictable events) and stochastic events (random catastrophic events like sylvatic plague or canine distemper). Ferret habitat has been greatly reduced and fragmented over the last century. The remaining small and isolated population(s) are highly susceptible to extinction from stochastic reasons alone. The plague and distemper epidemics at Meeteetse in 1985 illustrate this point perfectly. It is clear that every effort must be made to build a living nucleus of captive-bred ferrets safe from the vagaries of nature. It may be possible to then transplant ferrets back to the wild in small groups at secure reintroduction sites.

One critical question facing scientists attempting to recover ferrets is a very basic genetic one: Will there be a sufficient diversity of genetic material to insure the adaptability of any future wild populations? Inbreeding can have crippling effects upon isolated, chronically small mammal populations. In the past, inbreeding among the royal families of Europe in the eighteenth century and among certain isolated rural families in more recent times has led to such conditions as insanity and retardation. Certain domestic dog breeds, such as the St. Bernard, have been weakened by excessive inbreeding. Some researchers have postulated that the black-footed ferrets captured in South Dakota for the original captive breeding program were suffering the ill effects of inbreeding as they displayed such hereditary afflictions as diabetes and cancerous tumor growth. There is some concern about the genetic diversity of the remaining ferrets at Meeteetse.

A rule of thumb currently being used by some biologists is the 50/500 rule, a rule that suggests how many ferrets are needed to stave off extinction. The rule says that fifty breeding adults are necessary for a short-term viable population, and five hundred are necessary for the heterozygosity (genetic diversity) needed for ordinary evolutionary processes to occur. Several scientists using conservative genetic analysis have estimated that a breeding population of two hundred ferrets is needed for the short-term fitness of a ferret population. Others favor one hundred. There is some disagreement on the numbers. One scientist has suggested that, because carnivores are typically homozygous, genetic problems may be of less concern than other environmental factors to their survival.

Another theory that may be valuable to scientists working to save the ferret is the "metapopulation concept." As Dr. Clark writes:

> Many prairie dog complexes, each representing a patch of habitat, are irregularly distributed over the landscape. They vary in size and can support ferret populations of various sizes (most below 200 ferrets). This whole group of distinct populations can be viewed as a *population of populations, or a metapopulation* [author's emphasis]. For ferrets, species extinction is the equivalent of its extinction on all patches or prairie dog colony complexes. Ferret recovery will entail maintaining many small ferret populations, most below 200 individuals, over many habitat patches throughout their former range. Effective species conservation will require an understanding of the process of local extinction in patches of various sizes, and ferret recovery must be viewed as a metapopulation management challenge.

The metapopulation concept will be valuable only if that "living nucleus" of captive-bred ferrets is created, from which large groups of twenty or more ferrets may then be transplanted into a variety of secure areas.

The history of the Meeteetse ferret population, from its thrilling discovery in 1981 to its heartbreaking decline in 1985, provides conservationists with an invaluable case study. This study has particular relevance for other states, including Colorado, should new populations be found. Such case studies can provide much-needed lessons and insights for researchers and managers on how best to undertake, and successfully complete, the recovery of endangered species. In the case study of the Meeteetse ferret population, analysis reveals several organizational problems and instances of a flawed decision-making process that contributed (along with the plague and distemper) to the present situation. The model here is, regrettably, not one of how to insure success, but, rather, of how to court disaster.

Decision-making flaws began creeping in to ferret conservation efforts even as they began. As early as 1982, some conservationists warned the state and federal agencies that a catastrophic epidemic might devastate the Meeteetse ferrets. For this reason, and because the population was producing a surplus, these biologists formally recommended in 1983 and 1984 that at least ten ferrets be removed for captive breeding at the federal facility in Patuxent, Maryland, the mustelid breeding facility at Washington State University, or at other locations available at the time. The state and federal agencies vetoed this proposal, which had wide support among some scientists.

The breakdown between research and management is recognized in the June 1986 resolution of the American Society of Mammalogists, which makes reference to two important failures at Meeteetse: the failure to remove a small number of ferrets in 1984 for captive breeding purposes, and the failure to take proper precautions in 1984 with the first group of captured ferrets, who were killed by distemper in state holding facilities. It was determined in the 1970s with the South Dakota ferrets that the species is one hundred per cent susceptible to canine distemper. The passage of resolutions by the general membership is a public statement of the official position of the American Society of Mammalogists. This resolution is an important statement of philosophy, and of criticism, by an objective outside group of scientists.

The most important analyses of decision making with the Meeteetse ferrets yet to emerge are those of Dr. Tim Clark. Because Dr. Clark conducted a significant amount of the ferret field research and has an intimate knowledge of the day-to-day history of the project, he is consequently in an excellent position, as active participant, to reflect upon the successes and failures of the recovery effort. He has written that for endangered species recovery programs to be most successful they need careful, explicit organization and management:

> Unfortunately, many recovery programs tend to follow bureaucratic models of rigid authority relationships, rules, roles, regulations, and "closed" decision-making. In contrast, the complexity, diversity, and uncertainty of the endangered species task environment calls for "organic" organizations, the opposite of mechanistic bureaucracies. Organic organizations are flexible, adaptive, open decision-making structures with emphasis on problem-solving.

There is little doubt but that the inherent flexibility of organic versus mechanistic organizations offers greater utility to endangered species recovery. Rigid authoritarian structures stifle the creativity and constructive discussion necessary among professional conservationists to meet the dynamic and complex problems inherent in endangered species recovery. What the endangered species task force most needs is constructive debate and the generation of creative alternatives.

Dr. Clark suggests that endangered species biologists and managers take a lesson in organizational management from other disciplines and refers to works such as T. J. Peters's and R. H. Waterman's *In Search of Excellence: Lessons from America's Best Run Companies*. In that book in particular, a very conservative element of society—the business community—has been shown the considerable benefits of maintaining flexibility, spontaneity, and creativity in their organizations. Another classic organizational study is Irving Janis's *Group Think: A Psychological Study of Foreign Policy Decisions and Fiascoes*. In that book Janis studies the relationship between decision making in the 1961 Bay of Pigs Operation and in the 1962 Cuban Missile Crisis. In the former case, "group think," or conformity thinking, prevailed. Dissent was stifled, sensible options were not fully considered, and the result was a major foreign policy disaster. In the latter case, the president, having learned his lesson, actively solicited — in some cases demanded — viable alternatives. The result was that America prevailed in a potentially explosive confrontation with the Soviet Union.

Such lessons from other disciplines in organizational sociology, operational structure, policy analysis, and crisis management have an indisputable value to scientists and managers in the natural resources area. Conservationists, particularly those working in the high-risk and high-stakes world of endangered species, would do well to learn a few of these lessons. As Dr. Clark writes:

> Today, endangered species programs may involve 10 or more organizations (state, federal, private nonprofit, and others), each with a somewhat different history, domain, strategy, resource base, structure, culture/ideology, management mode, and so on, and ranging from rigid mechanistic (bureaucratic) to flexible organic (participative) structures and operational modes. Because of the inherent high uncertainty, high stakes, and high risk of the endangered species task environment, interorganizational conflict and program politicization may result as interests differentiate and each organization seeks to legitimize its own efforts — unless organizational coalitions can be appropriately designed and coordinated to reflect the actual interdependencies.

As an organizational model, Dr. Clark offers a "parallel organization" design, which "cuts across existing bureaucratic hierarchical structures and functional distinctions." It serves to supplement bureaucracy and exist side by side with it, not replace it. While being somewhat independent (and consequently more responsive and flexible), it does not undercut managers, nor does it replace their functions. It offers both more rapid problem solving and program implementation, attributes beneficial in any endangered species recovery effort, whether it be the panther in Florida, the condor in southern California, or the ferret in Wyoming. The breakdown between research and management that occurred in Wyoming over the ferret was but a symptom of flawed organizational structure, deeply rooted in an antiquated and inefficient set of relationships. It is to be hoped that the "parallel organization" suggested by Dr. Clark as a solution for this problem will be further studied and used in the future.

Finally, the ferret recovery effort at Meeteetse has involved a very high degree of conservation-community participation. While the input of federal and state agencies has been well publicized, the role played by the non-profit conservation community has not been as visible, but has been significant. This important nongovernment participation has occurred in several other recovery efforts as well, and may indicate the future direction of such programs, particularly as federal funding dwindles.

All of the lessons presented in the past few pages should be studied by researchers and managers in Colorado and elsewhere before new ferrets are found. These lessons are also applicable to other endangered species recovery efforts.

The ferret captured the attention and imagination of the nation and the world in 1986. In the first six months of the year, major articles on the situation in Meeteetse appeared in *Natural History, Defenders, Audubon, The New York Times, Animal Kingdom, The Washington Post*, and elsewhere. An hour-long television documentary was broadcast in June 1986. A once obscure and little known mammal has found itself the object of intense concern as we try to save it from slipping over the edge. The question is, has all of this attention come too late? Some believe so. Many believe that our failures at Meeteetse have sobering implications. Dr. Robert May, a world-renowned scientist at Princeton University, recently observed rather grimly in an article in *Nature* magazine:

> If such a mess can be made of efforts to save a creature as attractive as the black-footed ferret in a country as well organized and prosperous as the United States, prospects for conservation in other parts of the world are indeed bleak.

Others, like Dr. Clark and myself, are perhaps more optimistic about eventual ferret recovery, and believe that, with proper study of the Meeteetse experience, we can hone our skills to better meet endangered species challenges of the future. That the task is formidable no one denies. In one of his papers, Dr. Clark quotes the Australian scientists O. H. Frankel and M. E. Soule, who wrote in their book *Conservation and Evolution* of the difficulties facing conservationists:

> We are soldiers in a war and soldiers must be pragmatists. Thus our tenet that crude initiatives based on rough guidelines are better than the paralysis

of procrastination induced in some scientists by the fear of inadequate data. To delay the implementation of conservation and management programs until we have a definitive understanding of all complexities of the evolutionary process is analogous to allowing cancer to go untreated until we can prevent it . . . By the turn of the century most options will be closed. . . . It behooves us, therefore, to give serious and humble attention to all points of view and to be willing to compromise.

The removal of ferrets in 1984 from Meeteetse would be, as Frankel and Soule phrase it, a "crude initiative based on rough guidelines." Recovery efforts must somehow be both the hare and the tortoise: speedy and responsive, and yet deliberate and purposeful. Only with that synthesis can we win the race against time and species extinction.

The long story of the ferret over the last few decades draws to a close in this narrative, but, it is to be hoped, not in nature. Like the five blind men and the elephant, scientists studying the ferret have groped in a frustrating darkness, struggling to picture a greater whole of which they can only perceive isolated surface fragments. The first research questions asked twenty years ago in South Dakota were only a small beginning. So little was known of ferret ecology in the 1960s, 1970s, and even up to the early 1980s. We now know considerably more about the life of the "masked bandit of the prairies," but much more needs to be learned. Above all we need to find more ferrets!

The picture of the ferret that has emerged so far is of a small carnivorous mammal that is an active participant in the ecology of prairie dog colonies. The ferret was placed by the forces of nature on the original script of the Great Plains and the Intermountain West, listed somewhere (we're not sure where) on the dramatis personae. Remove Horatio, and the play *Hamlet* still remains. But the whole has been diminished by the excision. The question remains, with the bison, wolf, elk, grizzly, and others all taken from the plains—just how much more cast cutting can the drama take? The ferret poses this question, and more.

And if we ever do get a Shortgrass Prairie National Park (or Preserve), similar in size and scope to the Tall Grass Prairie National Preserve planned by the National Park Service for the Osage Hills of Oklahoma, it should have black-footed ferrets in it. Several hundred at least. A viable self-supporting population (or, more properly, set of populations). People should be able to take self-guided tours through the prairie dog colonies and, with a little luck near dusk or dawn, see a ferret (as they do now with the sage grouse at the courtship grounds in North Park, near Walden, Colorado, or with the beaver and waterfowl on the wooden walkways over the beaver ponds in Rocky Mountain National Park). The ferrets are a part of our national heritage, part of the epic history of the Great Plains and of America. They were there in 1823 when James Fenimore Cooper wrote *The Prairie*, thus beginning our long love affair with the plains. And they were there in 1952 when A. B. Guthrie, Jr. published *The Way West*, a chronicle of the early plains later made, like so many novels of the prairie, into a successful film. As a lively member of our native grasslands, the ferret should be an integral part of any long-awaited Shortgrass Prairie National Park or Preserve.

A Shortgrass Prairie National Park or Preserve, located somewhere in the rain shadow of the Rockies, could have many benefits not the least of which would be economic. Two feasible locations in Colorado would be in the vicinity of the historic Pawnee Buttes on the Pawnee National Grasslands in northeastern Colorado, or near the Purgatoire River on the Comanche National Grasslands in southeastern Colorado. Both sites could focus upon the original Plains Indians, the Oregon or Santa Fe Trail, early settlement and agriculture, the Dust Bowl, and modern agricultural and energy development. Such a park or preserve could also provide a natural location for a population of transplanted black-footed ferrets, a place to tell the story of how one of the world's most endangered mammals was almost lost for good, and then brought back from the edge. Conversely, a surrogate population of Siberian polecats would tell the opposite story. It is to be hoped such a park or preserve will one day become a reality. As Wallace Stegner once wrote, in his "Wilderness Letter": ". . . the vanishing prairie is as worth preserving for the wilderness idea as the alpine forests."

The real conservation test is yet to come. If other ferret populations are found in western North America (as I believe they will be), nature will have given us another chance. Will we have learned the lessons for successful conservation? Will research and management, state and federal agencies, private and public interests work together cooperatively, creatively, and courageously to meet the common challenge? Only time will tell. Perhaps it will not happen. Perhaps the ferret, for all our hopes and prayers, will disappear. But one thing is certain: If ferrets are found, our joy must be tempered with resolve. If the discovery occurs in Colorado, as it might, we must avoid the misfortunes of Wyoming. And if the ferret is gone, we must then work hard to apply its bitter lessons to the other mammals in this book, or else risk losing them too, one by one.

V

BLACK TIMBER

THE WOLVERINE

The wolverine is a tremendous character. No one can approach the subject of his life and habits, without feeling the same sort of embarrassment one would feel in writing of Cromwell or Tamerlane. Here, we know, is a personality of unmeasured force, courage, and achievement, but so enveloped in mists of legend, superstition, idolatry . . . that one scarcely knows how to begin.

          —Ernest Thompson Seton, *Lives of Game Animals*

INTRODUCTION

The Flattops is the area of Colorado I most associate with the wolverine. Perhaps it is the singular physiography—those distinctive gray ramparts so reminiscent of the dramatic wall formations in the northern Rockies—or maybe it is the classic subalpine habitat—mile after mile of beetle-killed spruce stands interspersed with small clear lakes, wide grass parks, and highland bogs—that so reminds me of the scenery of the north country. One September I rented a horse for a day at Trapper's Lake Lodge, and took the trail from Trapper's Lake, which is on the northern boundary of the Flattops Wilderness Area, up to Wall Lake, located about five miles to the south and a thousand feet higher in elevation. Throughout the day I was continually struck by the suitability of the area for the wolverine, an animal that requires a boreal habitat, plentiful numbers of ungulates and smaller mammals, and little interference from man.

Subalpine forest habitat on the edge of the Flattops Wilderness Area in Rio Blanco County. Several components of wolverine habitat can be seen here, including meadowland, spruce-fir forest, and aspen groves. Vaughn Lake, left of center, is at approximately 9,800 feet. Wolverines were historically present in this area, and may still exist in the region. *John Murray*

The Flattops offer all of this. The habitat is certainly there: dense, often impenetrable coniferous forests, broken rocky hillsides, rolling expanses of open meadowland, deciduous woodlands, cold streams and lakes, and the wolverine's all-important marshland. The prey base is one of the healthiest in the state—the White River deer and elk herds. They summer in the Flattops and then in the late autumn drift down the valleys toward their ancient wintering grounds. Smaller mammals, such as rabbits, voles, gophers, marmots, pikas, chipmunks, ground squirrels, mice, and beaver provide ample alternate prey. Finally, the high plateau offers sufficient solitude for the wolverine, with human access often difficult or impossible, particularly during periods of foul or freezing weather.

On the day I rode up to Wall Lake, it was, despite the mid-September date, as cold and blustery as November. It was hard to believe, as I rode higher and higher up toward the rimrocks at the head of the side canyon, that elsewhere in the state, on the other side of the Divide, it was sunny and mild, with temperatures in the low seventies. Up on top, ice had formed a solid sheet across some of the smaller tarns, and the delicate bluebells were all frozen and hanging dead on their stalks. The wind blew the rain and sleet parallel to the ground, and the rosy finches huddled deep inside the alpine willows around the lakes. I noticed the ptarmigan were already getting their winter colors, and the upper parts of Trapper's Peak, above the 11,000-foot line, were covered with the season's first snow.

The only people out in the Flattops that day were a handful of determined bow hunters, patiently bugling up the profligate bulls, warming themselves around small campfires, or leading stubborn pack mules down steep trails. Wherever I rode it was a scene out of America's wilderness past: vast, melancholy marshes, somber pine forests black under the low gray sky, and lonely trails beckoning for travelers to wander off with them through the emptiness. I ran into one camouflaged bow hunter just as I turned back toward the lodge, peering into the far reaches of a sedge park with his binoculars. Judging from his stubble, he had been out for at least a week. Judging from his running nose and hacking cough, he was only good for a few more days up on top. I knew how he felt, for years before I had worked as a wrangler and then as a hunting guide on the other side of the Wilderness, at Budge's Resort on the South Fork. It is a wild, friendly place, the Flattops, and yet it is a realm hostile at all seasons to man. Even in midsummer it can snow on top. It is a place, as they say in the mountains, where there are two seasons: the Fourth of July and winter, a place in which the wolverine, "The Giant Weasel," as Seton called him, is supremely adapted to live.

Toward evening, as I rode the last mile through the forest back down to Trapper's Lake, I spotted some movement off in the gloom of a ravine. It was a pine marten, a fellow member of the wolverine's mustelid family, out for his evening hunt, and completely unaware of my presence on the trail above. I watched him for what seemed a very long time as he foraged, sniffed, poked, prodded, dug, chewed, studied, pulled, tugged, and went about his evening routine in the impossible tangle of dead and dying spruce. An arboreal, tree-loving creature, he leapt adroitly, balanced, poised, jumped, and landed again and again, like an Olympic gymnast, in the welter of moss and lichen-covered branches. My horse grew impatient after a while but still I wanted to stay. Seeing the pine marten there, I couldn't help but think of his relative, the wolverine. I tried to imagine how it would be to see a wolverine, but I could only imagine. The only wolverine I have ever seen was stuffed and in a diorama at the Denver Natural History Museum.

Finally, his hunt in the ravine concluded, the pine marten disappeared down a rotting tree trunk into the timber, and I let the old buckskin mare pick her way back down the trail to the ranch. A moment later, far above us on Ripple Creek Pass, a geologist threw an electric switch that detonated a charge in a deep seismic test hole drilled to probe for subterranean mineral deposits. The explosion thundered sharply through the gloaming silence, and the horse reared back and whinnied, momentarily surprised. I waited for a second charge, but none followed. Slowly the light rain began to change to light snow, and I continued on. A little while later, as I crossed the bridge over the inlet below Trapper's Lake, the horse's hooves sounding hollow on the wooden planks, a bull elk bugled in the basin behind the lake, his song echoing defiantly through the twilight: "A-a-a-a-ai-eeeeeeeeee-ough! e-uh! e-uh!" I couldn't help but think of the two—the seismic blast and the elk's bugle—as somehow emblematic of the conflict facing Colorado, the wilderness, and the wildlife in the years to come, a future in which the wolverine, and others like him, will survive only if we find a balance between preservation and development. In the long perspective, there will come a day when the oil and gas are all gone, exhausted and superseded by new energy sources, and when that day arrives, we want the wilderness to still be there, and the wolverine.

In fact, the wolverine possibly exists in small, widely scattered numbers in the area of the Flattops, and maybe in a few other locations, including the San Juan Mountains (north of Durango and southeast of Wolf Creek Pass) and north and west of Rocky Mountain National Park. Its numbers are probably pitifully small, and practically nothing is known of its ecology: behavior, population dynamics, demography, and habitat requirements. The wolverine is a valued historic member of Colorado's mountains, and, unlike some of the other species in this book, comparatively little effort would be required to remove it from endangered status. The Flattops are but one of several areas where the wolverine could be relocated, if interest in its recovery develops.

PAST HISTORY

It is generally believed that the wolverine stock descended from a Miocene member of the *Martes*, or marten genus. Four or five million years ago, during the Pliocene epoch, *Plesio gulo* appeared, a wolverinelike animal derived from a martenlike animal, but having less specialized dentition. After *Plesio gulo* came *Gulo schlosseri*, about 2.5 million years ago, a species of wolverine found in both the Old and New Worlds (Cumberland Cave, Maryland, dated at 1.7 to 1.8 million years ago). It is possible that *Gulo schlosseri*, like many other species, evolved in the New World, and then migrated back over Beringea into the Old World. About 800,000 to 1,000,000 years ago *Gulo gulo* appeared, with fossil records in both the Old and New Worlds (Wyoming, Colorado, Idaho, Montana, Yukon, Alaska, Pennsylvania, and Quebec). The only fossil record of the wolverine in Colorado is at the Chimney Rock Animal Trap in Larimer County, about thirty miles southwest of Laramie, Wyoming at about seven thousand feet elevation. The animal trap is a natural hole, a circular depression in Casper sandstone about nine feet deep and fifty feet wide, into which animals fell and were trapped. Wolverine skeletal remains taken from the Chimney Rock Animal Trap have been carbon 14 dated at 11,980 years, plus or minus 180 years. Other species found in the trap include the grizzly bear, gray wolf, pika, marmot, prairie dog, wood rat, porcupine, mountain lion, coyote, mink, marten, and striped skunk. It is thought *Gulo gulo* was a fairly recent arrival to North America, arriving during the late Pleistocene via ice-free corridors from Siberia, and taking up residence wherever there was suitable habitat.

The head of an adult wolverine. Notice the distinctive coloring, and the scarring over the nose. *Jim Halfpenny*

In the Old World, wolverines are still found in northern Europe, from Scandinavia eastward across the whole of Asia into Siberia and Kamchatka, wherever habitat and human habitation permit. In the New World, wolverines are found in most of their historic range in Canada, with some recession from former areas in the eastern and prairie provinces. They are considered rare in the contiguous American states, with populations presently reported in Oregon, Washington, Idaho, Montana, Wyoming, and, possibly, in Colorado and Minnesota. Wolverine numbers in some of these areas, such as Montana, are thought to be increasing as trapping has decreased. It is generally thought that the two species, *Gulo gulo* (Old World wolverines) and *Gulo luscus* (New World wolverines), are conspecific, rather than being two distinct genetic lines.

The wolverine was given the scientific name *Ursus luscus* by Linnaeus in 1766, a name that was changed to *Gulo luscus* by Sabine in 1823. *Gulo* derives from the Latin *gula*, or throat, which alludes to the creature's supposed gluttony, and *luscus*, which means half blind, refers to the wolverine's reputation for bad eyesight. Though long known in the Old World, the wolverine was first reported in the New World by the French explorer Lahontan (*New Voyages to North America*), in a journal entry dated May 28, 1687. Lahontan described a badgerlike creature killed by camp dogs on a marsh of the St. Lawrence River in present day Quebec. He calls the animal "Carcaioux," an appellation that was later to become, among French Canadians, "Le Carcajou." According to Seton, "Carcaioux" itself is probably a French corruption of the Canadian Indian name, perhaps derived from the Algonquin or Cree name "Okee-coo-haw-gew" or "Okee-coo-haw-gees."

The early French trappers soon discovered that wolverine fur is unique and consequently valuable as trim for parkas because it is moisture resistant; human breath does not condense and freeze upon it, as it does on lynx or bobcat fur. It was also valued for its beauty and for its rarity, the wolverine apparently having never been abundant. Seton states that during the ten-year period between 1752 and 1761 the Hudson Bay Company averaged 798 wolverine skins per year. One hundred years later, wolverine fur was still actively taken, with an average annual catch of 1,192 during the eighty-five year period from 1821 to 1905. At the 1906 London annual fur sales, again according to Seton, the highest price brought by a wolverine pelt was thirty-four shillings each ($8.16) for sixty-four first-class dark skins. More recently, during the period 1971–1977, an average of 876.5 wolverine skins were taken annually in Alaska (with an average of 33.4 yearly for Montana), commanding an average individual price of $124.50.

The wolverine also gained a reputation among fur trappers as a nuisance on the trail from its habit of following the trappers in order to rob trap lines and raid food caches. Seton cited several cases of wolverines that reportedly followed trappers for distances up to forty miles in order to steal their trap bait. Even when trapped, the wolverine proved itself a tenacious fighter, as Seton relates in one case in which a wolverine carried a trap for thirty miles before it was finally killed. No food cache in the North Country was considered secure from the wolverine unless it was built as solidly as a bunker. One wolverine-proof cache constructed by an Indian near Great Bear Lake was described as being elevated off the ground "ten or twelve feet" with the bark removed from the supporting posts, and the horizontal beams projecting some "two or three beyond each end." That such elaborate precautions had to be taken are a tribute to the wolverine's tenacity, and its remarkable ability to climb, dig, or bite through virtually anything made of wood in order to get at scarce food in the winter months.

Both David Armstrong and Edward Warren provide brief histories of the wolverine in Colorado. Apparently the animal has, as is universally the case across its range, never been as abundant as other carnivores, such as bears and wolves. Colorado probably represents the southernmost extension of its range in the Rockies, although it is possible the wolverines occasionally followed the Continental Divide south into New Mexico a short distance. The first mention of a wolverine in Colorado is in the diary of Captain George A. Jackson, who made the first discovery of gold in the Colorado mountains. Dated January 6, 1859, the entry reports as follows: "Carcajou came into camp while I was at fire. Dogs killed him after I broke his back with belt axe. H– –l of a fight."

Warren reports two specimens, now in the Denver Museum of Natural History, that were taken near Breckenridge on January 17, 1876, and on Pass Creek, in Summit County, on September 20, 1876. Other reports from Armstrong include the following: Routt County (Elk River, Soda Creek); Jackson County (west of Walden, Owl Mountain, Rabbit Ears Mountains at head of Arapahoe Creek); Larimer County (Chambers Lake, moraine south of Moraine Park); Rio Blanco County (between Meeker and Craig, six miles east of Meeker, between Meeker and Rio Blanco); Garfield County (Yampa River near the Flattops, north and east of Trapper's Lake, Trapper's Lake); Grand County (Gore Pass, head of Williams Fork); Boulder County (near Boulder); Park County (near Montgomery); Delta County (east end of Grand Mesa, West Muddy Creek); Gunnison County (Pilot Knob, headwaters of Gunnison River, vicinity of Gothic, Irwin, Tin Cup Mine,

Union Park, head of Comanche Gulch, northwest of Pitkin); Ouray County (west of Ridgeway); San Miguel County (Mt. Wilson; San Juan County (headwaters of Rio Grande); Hinsdale County (Lake City, Los Pinos, southeast of Silverton); Mineral County (Wagon Wheel Gap, Wolf Creek Pass, Pagosa Peak); Huerfano County (head of Huerfano River); and Archuleta County (near Pagosa Springs). In reviewing this list several areas are conspicuous: Jackson County, Rio Blanco County, Garfield County, Gunnison County, and several counties that run up into the San Juan Mountain complex. These areas also correspond with locations that would, even on cursory review, provide some of the better wolverine habitat in Colorado.

NATURAL HISTORY

The wolverine is one of the most elusive carnivores in the world. It inhabits regions climatically inhospitable to man—the taiga, high tundra, and subalpine habitats—and even in areas of comparatively high population actual numbers may be surprisingly few and widely scattered. Add to this the fact that it prefers to wander alone, or occasionally in pairs, over a vast territory, and the problem of acquiring concrete ecological data becomes a formidable challenge. Because of its solitary habitats, small numbers, and severe habitat, most of our early knowledge was derived from the observations of fur trappers in the Far North, and from the journals of amateur naturalists. John Richardson mentioned the wolverine in his book *Fauna Boreali Americana*, as did John James Audubon and the Reverend Bachman in their work *Quadrupeds of North America*. Other authors who discussed the wolverine include MacFarlane in his *Notes on Mammals Collected and Observed in the Northern Mackenzie River District, Northwest Territories of Canada* (1905), and Walter Fry in *The Wolverine* (1923). Ernest Thompson Seton was the first naturalist to attempt a synthesis of this material, devoting forty-four pages to the wolverine in *Lives of Game Animals*. Much of Seton's information was based on historical sources in Canada and Alaska. No real scientific field work had yet been done.

Adolph Murie conducted extensive studies of the Alaskan timber wolf and grizzly bear in Mt. McKinley National Park, from 1922 to 1970. Despite the fact that he spent many thousands of hours in wolverine habitat, he only rarely saw the wolverine. He reported the wolverine to be "relatively scarce" and "secretive," recording only a handful of sightings in almost half a century. Most notable were incidents in which a wolf was seen chasing a wolverine up a tree near a moose carcass, and another occasion in which a wolverine turned and ran at maximum speed to avoid contact with a grizzly bear. Murie reported wolverine feeding on carrion, primarily carcasses of sheep, caribou, and moose, but had little more to offer on its lifestyle and ecology. This is typical of much of our knowledge of the animal through the 1950s. Since that time, research has been conducted in such locations as Siberia, Lapland, Alaska, Montana, and Canada, but much more needs to be learned about the natural history of this fascinating mammal.

The wolverine is the largest land member of the weasel family and belongs to the Mustelidae, or weasel subfamily. The Mustelidae are stout bearlike animals with bushy tails, hairy soles, short ears, and partly retractile claws more suited for climbing than for digging. Color is generally a deep blackish brown, pale and grayer on the crown and cheeks, with a stripe of pale red or pale brown beginning on each shoulder, passing backward along the sides, and uniting at the base of the tail. The throat and chest have a large irregular white patch. Claws, about an inch to an inch-and-a-half in length, are of a whitish horn color. Biologist Don E. Wilson, in the summary account he wrote of the species in Feldhammer and Chapman's *Wild Mammals of North America*, provides an excellent physical description of the species:

> The external appearance of the wolverine is more like that of badgers and skunks than like other members of the family Mustelidae, such as weasels (*Mustela* sp.) or otters (*Enhydra* and *Lutra*). The heavy body and lumbering gait may give a false impression of clumsiness. The head and tail are carried lower than the somewhat arched back. Although the head resembles the genus *Martes*, it seems broader and more rounded. The jaws are almost canidlike . . . The eyes are small and wide set. The ears are short, rounded, and well furred . . . The underfur is coarse, kinky, wooly . . . The guard hairs are . . . long, giving an overall shaggy appearance . . . The legs are stocky and powerful, and the feet large.

Wolverines average about forty inches in length, with the tail another eight to nine inches. Males are generally larger than females. Both males and females have anal scent glands that secrete a very pungent scent. The hind foot of the wolverine ranges up to seven inches in length. The forefoot is shorter, around five inches in length. Both feet average around four to five inches in width and display in tracks five toe pads around the sole and five corresponding claw marks.

Wolverine sign in the wild includes tracks, particularly visible over fresh snow, scent-marked carrion, scratch trees, and natal den sites. Don Wilson reports that "the belly may leave a drag mark in heavy snow." He further notes that wolverines apparently have a single molt between August and December. Wolverine fur could conceivably be found on trees, rocks, and forest debris at that time, and would be another indicator of the species. Wolverine dens are built by the female shortly after parturition. Because wolverines inhabit primarily boreal forests and are mostly nocturnal, it is difficult to see them or their sign, even in areas in which they may have relatively dense populations. Biologist Tom Beck says that researchers in Montana were recently surprised to discover a high wolverine population in an area of considerable human activity—the North Fork of the Flathead River near Glacier National Park. Wolverines had been previously thought to be scarce in this area. Interestingly enough, a comparative study of wolverine habitat in the Bob Marshall-Great Bear Wilderness found the same or fewer numbers of wolverines.

Don Wilson describes wolverine habitat as follows:

> Wolverines are primarily found in boreal forests, but there are many reports from open tundra areas in the far north. They are particularly fond of marshy areas, and are most at home in regions with snow on the ground during winter. The snow makes it easier for them to obtain large prey. They are found at a wide variety of elevations, and in the southern parts of their range are limited to montane areas. In California they are found in Douglas fir, mixed conifer, and lodgepole pine forest types (Schempf and White 1977). These authors listed 1,300 feet as the lowest elevational record for wolverines in California.

In the Rockies, wolverines have been found in the lower sagebrush and oakbrush communities, areas ungulates use as winter range. In Colorado, most wolverine sightings have been at higher altitudes, but at least several observations have been made at lower elevations in the last ten years. It is likely that wolverines historically used a greater portion of Western Slope Colorado than is reflected in reported observations. As biologist Tom Beck has informed me:

> . . . written records of early wildlife distribution and/or relative abundance were not a result of systematic searches. Often animal observations were a function of where man's early activities were concentrated.

Wolverine habitat in Colorado, while not as ideal as regions to the north (particularly in Canada and Alaska), clearly was, and probably remains, sufficient to sustain the species at the southern extension of its range in the Rockies.

It is thought that wolverines mate during the winter and early spring. Like river otters, grizzly bears, and black-footed ferrets, wolverines experience delayed implantation of the blastocyst. It is not known what advantages this has for the wolverine. Wilson says that most young are born in February or March, after a period of gestation ranging from 215 to 272 days. The period of active gestation ranges from thirty to forty days. In Alaska, litter sizes averaged 3.5 in one study; in Lapland the average was 2.6. Female wolverines are believed to breed no more often than every other year, according to Wilson, "possibly owing to a lengthy period of postweaning maternal care." Young animals, again according to Wilson, have been seen leaving the natal den in April and May. Weaning apparently begins at about seven to eight weeks, and adult size is reached by early winter. Wolverines are believed to live about eight or ten years in the wild. Zoo animals have lived as long as fifteen years.

Wolverines are highly mobile and live in extremely large home territories. Males have larger territories than females, and appear to exclude other males from their territories, but will permit females to enter. According to Wilson, females are mutually intolerant of one another. Male territories may extend up to twelve hundred square miles. Female home territories may extend up to 320 square miles.

Over these enormous areas wolverines have diverse food habitats, and feed on everything from small rodents to large ungulates. A Norwegian study cited by Wilson found the most important winter food for wolverines was reindeer, followed in order by moose, roe deer, fox, hare, small rodents, birds, and plants. This was also found to be the case in a Russian study. Researchers in Alaska found walrus, seals, and whales as important carrion items for wolverines. They also discovered that berries were eaten in the summer. In Sweden, it was discovered that "wolverines fed extensively on wasp larvae and berries of all types in the summer." It seems likely that wolverines are opportunistic animals, and will feed on just about anything they can find. Naturally, they prefer the larger ungulates, because there is more to eat on them. Some studies have found that, despite their relatively small size, wolverines (whose name derives from the Old French plural for wolves) can singlehandedly bring down the larger ungulates. They may also feed on kills made by other animals, such as bears and wolves. Deer, elk, and moose would be particularly vulnerable to wolverine attack when deep snow hinders their movement. Wolverines also apparently bury their prey in hidden food caches.

Causes of natural mortality among wild wolverine populations are not well known. Clearly the greatest enemy of the wolverine is man. Fortunately, as wolverines have become endangered and received protective status under the law, their numbers appear to be increasing in some areas where trapping and hunting them have been banned.

CURRENT STATUS AND FUTURE RECOVERY

Almost ninety years after Colorado achieved statehood, the season was finally closed on the wolverine as a furbearer, in 1965. Eight years later, in 1973, the wolverine was classified as an Endangered Species in Colorado. Several years after that, in 1978, the Colorado Division of Wildlife initiated a Wolverine Verification Project designed to document the past history of the species in Colorado and to determine its current status. This process was thorough and painstaking and involved a careful review of museum material as well as published and unpublished historical records. Over three thousand "wanted" posters of the wolverine were distributed throughout the state and a standardized report form was created for all wolverine sightings. Finally, several study sites were selected, based on areas that appeared promising from reports. Baited hair snags (hardware cloth cylinders with barbed wire interiors) were placed at likely locations in Jackson, Gunnison, Garfield, and Chaffee counties.

Throughout the study, a total of 265 reports of wolverine sightings were analyzed, of which only three were listed as positive. The overwhelming majority, 208, were considered to be nonwolverine reports. There were eighteen probable reports and thirty-six possible reports. Eight of these reports are worthy of inclusion here: 1) Three imported wolverines have escaped from Cheyenne Mountain Zoo since 1964, two of which were shot and killed, and the third of which has never been found; 2) In July 1977, a wolverine skull was found on the East Fork of the Cimmaron drainage in Gunnison County and estimated to be less than ten years old; 3) In June 1978, three photographs were taken of an animal, which seemed to be a wolverine, crossing a snow field on Trinchera Peak in the Sangre de Cristo Range; 4) In June 1978, an adult and three young animals, thought to be wolverines, were photographed west of Lake City; 5) In October 1978, two wolverines were released during filming for a movie near Aspen, Colo-

WANTED

INFORMATION ON THE WOLVERINE,

An Endangered Mammal In Colorado

The wolverine, largest member of the weasel family, usually feeds on carrion. They often travel in pairs and have very large territories.

TRACK MEASUREMENTS

length

hind

width

front

PAW PRINTS

measurements do not include claws

side

sometimes only four toes show

walking pattern

group

intergroup

straddle

gallop pattern

Information is also desired in all Colorado Lynx sightings.

APPEARANCE: Looks like a small bear b with a bushy tail; 30-40 inches in length i cluding tail; weighs up to 40 lbs.; dark brow with two yellowish stripes that merge abov the tail.

PROBABLE LOCATIONS: Isolated high-moun tain areas of Colorado.

CHARACTERISTICS: Moves with a bumpin and bouncing gait.

If possible, a good sighting should include:
* a photo or drawing;
* a photo of tracks with a scale included;
* a drawing of the tracks or trail;
* droppings; and/or
* date, time and location.

YOUR COOPERATION AT REPORTING SIGH INGS OF THIS MAMMAL WILL STRENGTHEN PROGRAM AIMED AT PRESERVING THE WO VERINE. WE NEED YOUR HELP!

NOTE: This animal is endangered and is pr tected by law.

If seen, please write or call the Colorado Division of Wildlife as soon as possible.

COLORADO DIVISION OF WILDLIFE — Nongame Section — P

6060 Broadway, Denver, Colorado 80216 • 825-1192

Posters such as this one were circulated by the Division of Wildlife during the Wolverine Verification Project to heighten public awareness of this rare and endangered mammal. *Jim Halfpenny*

The wolverine killed in March 1979 by Robert Kay of Vernal, Utah. Kay allegedly killed the wolverine a mile west of the Colorado-Utah border near U.S. Highway 40. However, since wolverines roam over ten miles per day, the animal may well have come from Colorado. *Jim Halfpenny*

rado, with sightings reported in the vicinity since then (the animals were imported from Canada); 6) In March 1979, a person shot a wolverine about a mile west of the Colorado-Utah border on U.S. Highway 40 (there is reason to believe the animal came from Colorado); 7) In March 1979, three employees of the Colorado Division of Wildlife watched an animal that they believe was a wolverine for three minutes at approximately seventy-five feet near the Rifle Colorado Fish Hatchery; and 8) In June 1979, a bear hunter for four minutes watched an animal approach his bear bait near Parshall at less than thirty feet, an animal he reported as a wolverine.

The researchers concluded their study by stating that:

> We believe wolverines continue to exist in Colorado. However, irrefutable proof of viable populations is absent due to difficulty in detection and obtaining positive proof. Even if positive proof of a wolverine were obtained, it would not prove the existence of a viable population.

Although the researchers were unable to verify the existence of a viable wolverine population, they were able to hypothesize about wolverine ecology in the state, based on areas in which reports were clustered. During the winter months, for example, it seems likely that wolverines would be more often found in northwestern Colorado, especially southeast of Meeker and north of Rifle, and in southwestern Colorado, especially north and east of Durango. Important habitat in the summer months could be the Flattops, northwestern Rocky Mountain National Park, and the San Juan Mountains. Many reports are found, for example, in the vicinity of the heavily traveled Wolf Creek Pass area. Another area might include the Sangre de Cristos because of the photos taken there. The Colorado Division of Wildlife final report on the wolverine verification states the following:

> If we assume that at least some of the wolverine reports received by the project are true, we may hypothesize about the ecology of wolverine in Colorado today. The wolverine usually travels alone, although some may be reproducing as evidenced by reports of young. The wolverine is very secretive and most observers surprise the animal, obtaining but a short glimpse (less than 1 minute) at a short distance (less than 150 feet). During the warmer months, May through October, the wolverine occurs primarily at higher elevations from the upper montane to the tundra regions. A portion of their diet may consist of marmot during the summer. Starting around November, at least some wolverine may start an elevational migration to the lower limits of treeline or their movements within their ranges are great enough to reach low elevations. These migrations probably follow wintering ungulate herds and may go down into the oakbrush-sagebrush zone. The distribution of winter reports suggests that the animals may favor major south-facing slopes or drainages.

It is generally believed in the scientific community that wolverines continue to exist in Colorado, but that because the populations are small and scattered, and wolverines are inherently secretive, proof of their existence is virtually impossible to obtain. One thing that is certain with respect to wolverines is that it is important to protect ungulate winter range, an important component of their habitat. Winter range is continually being lost throughout Colorado, as resort developments closely associated with ski areas spread downvalley from the ski slopes.

The wolverine strikes some as a logical candidate for a recovery project, a plan similar to that currently in effect for the river otter. The objective of a wolverine recovery would be to restore it to one or more areas of secure and suitable habitat, such as can be found in the Flattops, Rocky Mountain National Park, and the San Juan Mountains. Opponents of such an effort argue that the wolverine was a peripheral species in Colorado, an animal at the southern range of its habitat in the Rockies. They question the wisdom of a wolverine reintroduction, and also wonder if scarce funds might be better spent elsewhere, such as on the river otter recovery. Proponents of a wolverine recovery say that because the wolverine was part of the original biota of Colorado, and because we have the habitat and the scientific capability to restore the species, an effort should be made at restoration. They point out that the cost of such a project would be small, and its benefits manifold, ranging from increased visibility for nongame wildlife in Colorado to restoring an "indicator species" of the pristine quality of boreal habitats. Also, the argument can be raised that the river otter, for all we know, might also have been a peripheral species in Colorado. There are a paucity of historical records for both species.

Two wolverines (seen here in cages) were released in October 1978 by Stouffer Productions of Aspen while filming a wildlife movie. The wolverines, which were imported from Canada, were released east of Castle Peak in Pitkin County in the Maroon Bells-Snowmass Wilderness area. Three reports in the general vicinity since their release may relate to these animals. John Denver is in the sheepskin coat to the far left. *Jim Halfpenny*

Dr. Jim Halfpenny, the University of Colorado research biologist who participated in the Colorado Wolverine Verification Project, is among those who have suggested that a wolverine recovery plan be formulated. He believes it would not be difficult to transplant a number of wolverines into selected areas in Colorado, a number sufficient to establish a viable population. There are, he tells me, at least three areas—the Flattops, Rocky Mountain National Park, and the San Juan Mountains—that probably offer the essential components of wolverine habitat: a wilderness location, a boreal ecosystem, and an adequate prey base. An additional advantage of such a project to scientists would be that the released wolverines could be fitted with radio collars and carefully monitored. As a result, more could be learned about wolverine ecology and natural history. Such a study would make an interesting thesis or dissertation project for a graduate wildlife-biology student at Colorado State University or the University of Colorado.

There are a number of approaches that could be taken by a group of people interested in wolverine recovery in Colorado, from working alone on the project to working in concert with the Division of Wildlife or the National Park Service, to leaving the project entirely up to either one of those two agencies. It seems to me the first order of business for these people would be to create a group, a "Colorado Wolverine Society." This society would be similar in organization and objective to the "Rocky Mountain Bighorn Society" or the "Desert Bighorn Society," both of which have been actively involved in bighorn restoration projects in Colorado and Arizona, respectively. Such a group would probably find an immediate grassroots constituency among a wide variety of groups in Colorado, ranging from corporations interested in tax-deductible donations to environmentally aware individuals interested in wildlife issues. A distinguished board of directors would be helpful in terms of fund raising, and a scientific advisory council could assist in strategic biological decisions. The Colorado Wolverine Society could raise funds through the standard techniques employed by nonprofit organizations: bumper stickers, tee-shirts, photographs, guest speakers at dinners, corporate donations, and so on. A newsletter could help increase membership and disseminate information.

The choice will no doubt depend in part on how the Division of Wildlife or National Park Service respond to the idea of a wolverine recovery. If it could be demonstrated to them that there was a sincere and serious interest in wolverine recovery, it is likely their interest would deepen. Assuming that the issue reaches the stage at which there is mutual public and agency support, the next step would be to identify suitable release sites.

Many scientists believe that wolverines continue to exist in Colorado. Their future, however, may depend on the release of captive wolverines like this one to augment fragile populations. Such a release would be ideal in a location like Rocky Mountain National Park, where there would be no conflicts with trapping, hunting, or grazing. Wolverines could be radio-collared and carefully monitored to learn more about their ecology. *Jim Halfpenny*

One of the advantages of Rocky Mountain National Park would become clear at this point: there is no trapping, hunting, or grazing in the park, all areas of possible conflict with wolverines. Additionally, one of the objectives of the National Park Service is to preserve, and if necessary restore, pre-Columbian conditions in the parks. The restoration of the wolverine would be consistent with that management objective. After a complete environmental assessment, and the location and importation of healthy wolverine stock, the transplant could actually begin.

A wolverine recovery would find a broader base of support than a grizzly recovery or a wolf recovery. In fact, it may be that conditions will never advance sufficiently, politically and socially, to permit grizzlies and wolves to once again roam the wilds of Colorado. The wolverine, however, offers hope to conservationists interested in the recovery of threatened and endangered mammals in Colorado. Opponents will doubt the suitability of a wolverine recovery. They should be listened to—any recovery effort is doomed to failure if it does not respond appropriately to its critics. But it seems to me that both the wolverine and the lynx are strong candidates for recovery in Colorado. They are the next step up from the river otter—mammals that do not face the historic levels of "predator prejudice" that have been associated with species like the grizzly and wolf. They may be as close as we ever get to the return of all the mammals that lived in Colorado in the early twentieth century. It is possible that further study and analysis by a responsible group of researchers and managers produces a negative decision on wolverine recovery, but I doubt it. At the least, wolverine recovery is a viable possibility for nongame management, and one that merits serious examination. If successful, it might also get people used to having new animals around, and pave the way, one day, for the return of other species.

VI

SNOW COUNTRY

THE LYNX

The bear were all holed up for the winter, so our game was limited to cougar and bobcat. In the books the bobcat is always called a lynx, which it, of course, is; but whenever a hunter or trapper speaks of a lynx . . . he means a lucivee . . . Like all people of European descent who have gone into strange lands we Americans have christened our wild beasts with a fine disregard for their specific and generic relations.
— Theodore Roosevelt, *Outdoor Pastimes of an American Hunter*

INTRODUCTION

The Felidae, as a distinct animal family, are among the oldest and most successful carnivores in the world. Fossil remains of catlike animals date back well before the Pliocene. At least one Pleistocene feline, the saber-toothed cat unearthed in the La Brea Tar Pits of southern California, was remarkable for its enormous specialized canines, with the two upper teeth prominently descending well below the lower line of the jaw. Other, less specialized cats, took hold and flourished in the post-Pleistocene. Cats have since diversified and become one of the most widespread animal families on earth, inhabiting every ecosystem except glacial ice, high Arctic tundra, and true desert. With their retractile claws, sword-shaped canines, and solitary ambush method of hunting (with the exception of the African lion), cats are formidable predators, whether the thirty-pound North American lynx or the three-hundred-pound Siberian tiger.

Mankind has long known of and been fascinated with the felids. The deification of cats by the ancient Egyptians was most certainly antedated by many previous ages of domestication. Cheetahs accompanied the ancient Sumerians on their hunts as early as 3000 B.C., and were familiar hunting companions to the Egyptian pharoahs. The largest animal statue in the world, the Great Sphinx at Giza, built by Ramses II, portrays a lion with a man's head. The Bible mentions lions no less than 130 times as common mammals in ancient Palestine. In Greek mythology, the first of twelve labors ordered of Hercules by King Eurystheus was to kill the Nemean Lion, a terrible beast who ravaged the Valley of Nemea. Notably, the lion was extinct in Greece by 200 B.C., and by the time of Caesar, had to be imported into Italy from North Africa for the Coliseum "games."

Later, in the Middle Ages, in recognition of its power and beauty, the lion was placed on the royal crests of the kings of England, Scotland, Norway, and Denmark, and was incorporated into the coat of arms of Zurich, Luxembourg, Wales, and the city state of Hesse in Germany. Richard Coeur de Lion (1157–1200), King of England during the third crusade, was known as Lion-Hearted for, among other things, his remarkable bravery at the battle of Jaffa, in Palestine. Marco Polo (1254–1324), who visited the Kublai Khan at his summer residence in Karakorum, reported back to Europe that the Khan kept one thousand cheetahs for hunting purposes, equipped with hoods and used much as the Europeans used falcons for sport hunting in their game parks. Cheetahs became widely used by European royalty in the Middle Ages, including the princes of Old Russia, William the Conqueror, numerous French kings, and the Austrian Emperor Leopold I, who used them to hunt deer in the Vienna Woods. The use of cheetahs as hunting animals was equally widespread elsewhere, with their use reported in Arabia, Abyssinia, Armenia, Syria, Palestine, and India.

The felids, particularly the big cats, have long been familiar in literature, and references to them are found in sources as diverse as Homer and Yeats, from the beginning of written language to the present time. The lion, like the wolf, is mentioned frequently in *The Epic of Gilgamesh* as a primary predator on domestic herds. In book twelve of his epic poem *The Iliad*, Homer compares the bravery of the Trojan King, Hector, surrounded by Greek warriors, to that of a wild boar or lion, encircled by hunting hounds:

As when among a pack of hounds and huntsmen assembled a wild boar or lion turns at bay in the strength of his fury, and the men, closing themselves into a wall about him, stand up to face him, and cast at him with the volley-

ing spears thrown from their hands, and in spite of this the proud heart feels
not terror, nor turns to run, and it is his own courage that kills him; and
again and again he turns on them trying to break the massed men and
wherever he charges the masses of men break away in front of him; such
was Hector as he went through the battle . . .

Elsewhere, the literature of antiquity is full of references that bear tribute
to the big cats, with little of the peculiar revulsion we will see later in references to the wolf.

Throughout the Renaissance, the big cats were favorites of the English
dramatic poets, a popularity evidenced in these famous lines that Bottom
speaks in *A Midsummer Night's Dream*:

Let me play the lion too: I will roar, that I will do any man's heart good
to hear me. I will roar that I will make the Duke say, "Let him roar again;
let him roar again." 1.2.64–67.

More recently, the tiger became the object of one of the most famous
poems in the English language, "The Tyger," written by the English poet
William Blake in 1794, and containing the following two quatrains:

Tyger! Tyger! burning bright
In the forests of the night,
What immortal hand or eye
Could frame thy fearful symmetry?
●●●●●
When the stars threw down their spears,
And water'd heaven with their tears,
Did he smile his work to see?
Did he who made the Lamb make thee?

In the twentieth century, William Butler Yeats, the Irish Nobel-Prize-
winning poet, wrote of the Egyptian Sphinx in his well known poem "Second
Coming" (1920):

Troubles my sight: somewhere in sands of the desert
A shape with lion body and the head of a man,
A gaze blank and pitiless as the sun,
Is moving its slow thighs, while all about it
Reel shadows of the indignant desert birds.

Mounted specimen of a lynx trapped near Vail in Eagle County during the winter of 1973–74. The full body is on exhibit at the Division of Wildlife Headquarters in Denver. *Jim Halfpenny*

Yeats's fellow poet T. S. Eliot wrote a small book of poems entirely (and playfully) devoted to domestic cats: *Old Possum's Book of Practical Cats* (1939), which was developed into an immensely popular and successful Broadway musical in 1983. Each poem was the personal fable of a particular cat, as in "Growltiger's Last Stand":

> Growltiger was a brave cat, who lived upon a barge:
> In fact he was the roughest cat that ever roamed at large,
> From Gravesend up to Oxford he pursued his evil aims,
> Rejoicing in his title of "The Terror of the Thames"

The importance of the felids is clear. They have been well-heralded companions and adversaries of humankind since recorded history began, and long before that. Always, our conflicts with them have been tempered with admiration for their courage, intelligence, and physical beauty. In their mysterious love of solitude and lonely places, their well-known independence, and their impressive cunning and intelligence, the cats embody all that is forever elusive, wild, and untamable in nature. As if in testament to their puissance and magnificence, sculpted lions guard libraries, museums, forts, and public and private buildings around the world. It is indeed ironic, in this perspective, that despite our long acquaintance with and great love and admiration for the felids, we have made cats as a group among the most threatened and endangered animals in the world.

The list includes such species as the Siberian tiger, Asiatic leopard, Asiatic lion, jaguar, cheetah, snow leopard, clouded leopard, ocelot, jaguarundi, margay, pampas cat, caracal cat, South American jungle cat, Spanish (pardel) lynx, Florida panther, eastern mountain lion, and Canadian lynx. In almost every case, including the lynx in Colorado, the combined effects of hunting and trapping particularly for their beautiful pelts, and loss of critical habitat have been ruinous for the individual species. In the years to come, we can expect more and more cats to become endangered as more and more habitat is lost, particularly in the tropical rain forests of South and Central America, and elsewhere in the tropics where habitat is being lost to cultivation, grazing, logging, settlement, and mineral exploration and development.

Three wild felids are currently found in Colorado: the mountain lion, bobcat, and lynx. There is one report of a jaguar in the state, made by Rufus B. Sage in November, 1843 while exploring the Front Range, but it is believed he observed an immature mountain lion, which would be spotted. The northernmost authenticated records of jaguars are near Springer (Colfax

County), New Mexico, and in northcentral Arizona. All three of the native Colorado cats are extremely reclusive, primarily nocturnal, and consequently difficult to locate in the wild. I have never seen a lion in the wild, and after a good many miles both on and off the trails in Colorado, have still seen only two bobcats. The first I saw years ago while hunting near Bull Canyon in western Dry Creek Basin, and the other more recently while cross-country skiing on the lower Big Thompson River in Rocky Mountain National Park. Both sightings are probably typical: less than thirty seconds, less than thirty yards. I have occasionally found lion tracks and sign while rock hunting or fossil collecting on remote ridgetops or rock outcroppings. All in all, it is probably easier to see a black bear or a bald eagle in Colorado than it is to see any of the wild cats.

Late one summer, in keeping with a long list of summer projects, I hiked into an obscure mountain canyon in Grand County, a place, as I noted in my field journal at the time, that seemed to richly offer all that the lynx requires for life: an expansive spruce-fir forest; plentiful numbers of its primary prey, the snowshoe hare; and complete security and isolation from humans in all seasons of the year. In fact, researchers have identified Grand County as one of only seven counties in Colorado in which the Canadian lynx may still exist. Out of concern for its future, I won't mention the area specifically by name, but its brief description will be illustrative of the distinct boreal niche in which the lynx seems to have survived in Colorado. While it is not likely that lynx presently live in this particular location, they probably have in the past, and possibly could in the years to come.

It is a long rocky glacial canyon, ranging at either extreme from the upper montane to the alpine, with the great portion in subalpine forest. At its greatest extension it is perhaps nine miles in length, and encloses approximately twelve square miles of rugged terrain. On either side are large fortresslike formations of partially eroded bedrock, making penetration from the flanks extremely difficult. The only practical approach is directly up the middle of the canyon from a lower valley, a route that often necessitates hand-over-hand climbing through steep fields of broken rock and tangled forest beside roaring waterfalls, precipitous cliffs, and plunging cataracts. There are no maintained trails into the place. Its meadows have never been grazed by sheep or cattle. Its primeval forests have never been commercially logged.

In places, the spruce and fir form a thick canopy overhead, and the wind-throw of living and dead trees, draped with the gloomy fruticose lichen (*Usnea*) known as "old man's beard," make travel an ordeal to all but butterflies and bumblebees. In other areas, the forest opens up on large grassy

Subalpine forest habitat in Grand County. This is classic lynx habitat. The beaver pond in the lower right foreground is 9,600 feet. The alpine ridge in the background runs just under 12,000 feet. *John Murray*

clearings, small bogs, rocky hillsides, and small meadows brimming with bluebells, columbine, arnica, paintbrush, lupine, harebells, larkspur, and a few dozen other wildflowers. Through the middle of the canyon flows a small stream that is held in a series of tarns and lakes up higher, is briefly dammed and diverted by a family of beaver in the center, and forms a final pool at the edge of the last glacial bench before dropping, in a series of dramatic cataracts and waterfalls, to the dark valley far below. To a cat, I concluded, whether a high-ranging bobcat, a local puma, or a wandering lynx, this sort of remote and virgin high mountain habitat would be ideal. Most important to the lynx would be the snowshoe hares, whose sign was plentiful in the grassy clearings and meadows.

In such guarded places the lynx may, and likely does, endure in Colorado. The very ruggedness of such places insures their security. Human access is possible only a few months out of the year. In most years, according to the ranger with whom I spoke at the Granby District Office of the Arapahoe National Forest, fewer than six people take out permits to camp in the area. So long as areas like this survive, the lynx will continue to have a home in Colorado. There, in the cloud-drenched spruce-fir forests and sun-washed flower meadows, guarded by sheer ramparts, buttresses, pinnacles, and cyclopean turrets of rock, there, if anywhere, is the kingdom of the lynx.

PAST HISTORY

Fossil evidence from South Africa suggests that the lynx had an African origin in the early mid-Pliocene, about four million years ago. The ancestral lynx did not have the long legs of the modern lynx. Also, its head was significantly larger relative to body size than that of the lynx we know today. Both characteristics suggest the fossil lynx had a different hunting style. The ancient lynx subsequently migrated from Africa into the Northern Hemisphere, giving rise to an Asian lynx that eventually evolved into the modern lynx. This modern lynx migrated from Asia into Europe and North America. It is believed the bobcat evolved from lynx stock about 3.2 to 3.4 million years ago.

The fossil history of the lynx in North America is sparse, but remains have been found in Alberta, Alaska, Idaho, Utah, and the Yukon. Age on these fossils ranges to 100,000 years ago. The Chimney Rock Animal Trap in northeastern Colorado contains the fossil remains of the bobcat, mountain lion, and an extinct species of mountain lion, but not of the lynx.

Although the lynx probably inhabited Colorado at this time (about ten thousand years ago), there are, as yet, no fossil records to confirm this assumption. The almost exclusively boreal nature of its habitat probably contributes to the absence of fossilized remains.

The lynx is a Holarctic species, found in boreal regions of both North America and Eurasia. Most authorities believe that the Eurasian and North American lynxes are conspecific. The biologists Chet McCord and Jim Cardoza, in the summary account they wrote for the species in Feldhammer and Chapman's *Wild Mammals of North America*, described the present worldwide distribution of the lynx as follows:

> The species remains widespread in northern areas but has receded from much of its former range in the United States and western Europe. In Canada, the lynx is found from Newfoundland, Labrador, and Quebec west to central British Columbia and the Yukon. It is probably extirpated from New Brunswick, lower Nova Scotia, and Prince Edward Island, and is absent from unforested areas of the Ungava Peninsula and the Northwest Territories. The lynx is also found in mainland Alaska (except the Seward Peninsula and the panhandle) north to the tree line and in the contiguous United States in northern New England, parts of the Lake States, the Pacific Northwest, and parts of the Rocky Mountains south to Utah. . . . Currently the species is resident in limited areas of Scandinavia, Poland, Czechoslovakia, Yugoslavia, Rumania, and Greece. A disjunct population in southern Spain is now severely reduced in numbers and distribution and considered endangered. Stragglers occur rarely in the western Pyrenees of France. Lynxes also occur in parts of Iraq, Iran, Tibet, upper India, Mongolia, Manchuria, and western and northwestern China.

The authors further note that lynx are extremely widespread in the Soviet Union, and are found from the Polish border east to the Pacific Ocean (Kamchatka and Sakhalin islands).

The lynx, like the river otter and the wolverine, has long been trapped and hunted for its beautiful fur, which is particularly long and valued during the winter months. Throughout its range, lynx trapping has been somewhat hampered at times by the well-documented synchronous relationship between lynx numbers and snowshoe hare populations, which periodically undergo explosive increases and devastating crashes. This relationship is reflected in trapping records. In 1896, for example, the naturalist Ernest Thompson Seton reported that 56,407 lynx pelts were taken in trade in Canada. The number declined by a factor of approximately 10 to 4,473 in 1900 but then shot up to 58,850 in 1905 and 61,388 in 1906. The next year (1907) total lynx trapped declined to 36,201. In 1908 the figure had decreased to only 9,664.

The lynx was apparently never abundant in Colorado and seems to have reached its southernmost range in the Colorado Rockies. The lynx taken from Cumbres Pass in Conejos County late in the nineteenth century (just two miles north of the New Mexico boundary) could represent the southernmost range of the lynx in this part of the world. Both Edward Warren and David Armstrong discussed lynx distribution in their books and agreed that the animal was (and probably still is) confined, in the words of Warren, "to the heavy timber of our high mountains." Armstrong observes that "some early writers reported lynx as common in Colorado at some places. By 1900 reports of the species had grown less numerous." Loss of habitat has further restricted the lynx in Colorado. University of Colorado biologist Jim Halfpenny suggested in a recent article on lynx in Colorado that "human encroachment since 1920 has limited lynx distribution to above 2,730 meters [9,000 feet]." Armstrong noted that the protected status afforded the species by a change in hunting regulations in 1970 (expanded by state endangered species legislation in 1973) should reverse any trend toward extirpation if it "has not come too late."

The former distribution of the lynx in Colorado, while scattered, was probably extensive, and roughly coequal with boreal habitats. This is reflected in the diverse areas in which specimens have been found. Armstrong found specimens in the following Western Slope counties: Gunnison, Routt, Jackson, Rio Blanco, Garfield, Eagle, Grand, Summit, Pitkin, Park, Custer, San Juan, La Plata, and Archuleta. Present range, discussed more fully later in the chapter, possibly includes seven of those counties.

NATURAL HISTORY

As with the river otter, for many centuries all that was known about the ecology of lynxes was that which was needed to hunt and trap them successfully. Even the earliest trappers, though, noted the peculiar rise and fall in the population of wild lynx, which seemed to correspond with similar fluctuations in the numbers of its primary prey, the snowshoe hare. This was noted as early as 1799, in the journals of Canadian Alexander Henry, who observed the peculiar phenomena on the Upper Red River and reported that there was no evidence that it was related to any epidemics or disease, or to any sudden local migration of lynx out of the area. He suggested at the time that the fluctuations were possibly related to the failure of the rabbit population. This was probably one of the first truly scientific observations made of the lynx in the New World. Dr. John Richardson wrote of the lynx in his book *Fauna Boreali Americana* (1829), as did Audubon and Bachman in their *Quadrupeds of North America* (1849). In 1887 E. W. Nelson also described the lynx in his book *Natural History Collections Made in Alaska*. Ernest Thompson Seton assembled much of the natural history lore and anecdotal material about the lynx in his book *Lives of Game Animals* (1929). The naturalist Adolph Murie noted the relationship between the snowshoe hare and the lynx while researching the wolf and the grizzly bear in Mt. McKinley National Park in Alaska during the 1940s. Since that time, extensive research has been conducted in America, Canada, Scandinavia, and the Soviet Union that has added greatly to our knowledge of this mysterious and beautiful animal. We have come a long way from the recollections of trappers, with several intensive long-term studies providing fascinating insights into the complex ecology of the lynx. But much more needs to be learned.

The biologists Chet McCord and Jim Cardoza provide an excellent physical description of the lynx in their chapter in *Wild Mammals of North America*:

> In the lynx, as in the bobcat, the sexes are colored similarly, although individual variation may be apparent. Adult North American lynxes in prime winter pelage have long thick fluffy fur with the upper body parts generally grizzled grayish brown mixed with buff or pale brown. . .The top of the head is brownish, with the ears buffy brown externally with a central white spot and the tufts and margins black. The facial ruff and throat are a mixture of grayish white, black, and brown. Underparts, feet, and legs are grayish white or buffy white, sometimes sprinkled with brown or blackish brown spots, particularly on the insides of the legs. The tail is brownish or pale buffy white *with a completely black tip* [my emphasis]. . .There is apparently a single annual molt beginning in late spring. . .Color variations occur rarely in lynxes.

The tail of the lynx is completely black, unlike that of the bobcat, which is black only on the very tip. Also, the lynx has much larger feet than the bobcat, and they are well adapted to the heavy snows through which it must traverse at higher elevations. Another distinguishing characteristic is that the black ear tufts are much more prominent on the lynx than on the bobcat. Finally, mature lynxes are generally, but not always, larger than mature bobcats.

Two common Colorado cats that are often confused with the rare lynx are the mountain lion (above) and the bobcat (below). While the bobcat is closer in size to the lynx than is the lion, its shorter legs, smaller feet, and black-tipped tail distinguish it from its endangered cousin. *Greg Hayes (lion) and John Murray (bobcat)*

As with the other species in this book, lynxes are sexually dimorphic, with the males on average heavier than the females. Size does vary according to geography and climate, probably following Bergman's rule that the size of animals within a group is smallest in the south and largest in the north. According to McCord and Cardoza, the largest lynx ever reported was taken in central Russia and weighed slightly over seventy pounds. This lynx no doubt ate a lot of snowshoe hare (or was the result of several bottles of vodka). Normally, lynx weigh around twenty-five or thirty pounds, with forty considered by Ernest Thompson Seton an extremely large lynx.

Lynx sign most often encountered in the wild include tracks, particularly over snow, scats and scent posts, and kill sites. Lynx tracks are both larger and different in appearance than bobcat tracks. In the most recent study in Colorado, a researcher classified tracks greater than 3.4 inches wide, with a straddle less than 7.2 inches and a stride less than 17.2 inches (but only sinking shallowly into the snow) as being made by lynx. As do most cats, lynx use feces, urination, and front-foot scrapes as a means of communication in their territory. In one study cited by McCord and Cardoza, lynx were found to urinate on stumps, bushes, and other sites along the trail as much as twenty-seven to thirty-two times per kilometer. Lynx scat often contains the skeletal remains of its primary prey, the snowshoe hare. Ernest Thompson Seton reported that lynxes give birth in hollow logs, stumps, and clumps of timber. Murie reported a den in a dense spruce windfall in central Alaska. Lynx may also use daybeds.

Seton described the lynx as a denizen of the "unbroken forest," while the bobcat avoids "dense shade and deep snow" and seeks out more varied low country. Lynxes are most often found in large forests, typically spruce-fir stands interspersed with rock outcropping, bogs, and thickets. Deep snows accumulate in these areas, but the lynx is well adapted, with its large feet, to travel over the drifts. Bobcats, in contrast, with their smaller, almost dainty feet, tend to prefer the lower ranges of mountainous habitat. McCord and Cardoza made the following observations vis-à-vis lynx habitat:

In Alaska, lynxes were found in rolling hilly terrain . . . one-half forested with approximately equal portions of coniferous and deciduous forest. The coniferous area comprised stands of black spruce underlain by mosses and white spruce with an understory of alder and willow. White birch, quaking aspen, and cottonwood were major components of the deciduous forest. Mixed types of white spruce-white birch and white spruce-aspen were found along roads. Unforested tundra, comprising one-half the study area, was rarely used

by lynxes. . .Lynx habitat in western Newfoundland was characterized by
second-growth stands of balsam fir, black and white spruce, and white and
yellow birch interspersed with bogs and shrub barrens. . .Lynxes typically
were most active in the forested areas. . .In the Soviet Union, lynxes are
found chiefly in old-growth taiga.

Biologists studying lynxes and bobcats on Cape Breton Island, Nova
Scotia in 1955 made an important discovery about the importance of snow
depth to the distribution of the two species. As McCord and Cardoza report in their summation of the data:

> Before 1955 the island had only a lynx population, but with the building
> of a causeway to the mainland, the intervening strait began to freeze, thus
> allowing bobcats access probably for the first time. The bobcat dramatically
> increased in the lowlands where snow depths were minimal, but did not
> establish populations in the northern highlands sections where snow depths
> are much greater. Lynxes are now found only in the highlands. Apparently,
> the difference in snow depths between the highlands and lowlands is the only
> factor to explain the distribution of the two species.

Across their range, deep snow probably often limits the distribution of these
two similar species.

Although the lynx may occasionally eat such animals as grouse, ptarmigan, deer, squirrels, mice, and marmots, the species is almost exclusively
dependent on the snowshoe hare. One Canadian study cited by McCord
and Cardoza found that snowshoe hare comprised forty-three per cent of
the lynx diet in a period of hare scarcity, and one hundred per cent of the
lynx diet in a period of hare abundance. The authors also note a few instances of cooperative hunting efforts by lynx, particularly for large prey.

Lynx harvests for the period 1735–1950 in Canada show regular fluctuations, with the average period between peak years being 9.6 years. This
periodic cycle seems to correspond with the ten-year cycle observed in snowshoe hare populations. Seton reported several instances of lynx being found
in a state of extreme starvation during periods of hare scarcity. The lynx
is very susceptible to these population surges and collapses among its prey
base. McCord and Cardoza note that these cycles can result in the long-
range dispersal of lynx into alien habitats, and postulate that these periodic
irruptions may enhance species survival by encouraging gene flow between
isolated populations.

Lynxes mate in the spring. The gestation period is about sixty-three days (Seton reported a range of sixty to sixty-five days), with most births occurring from late May to early June. The young lynxes are believed to wean in about twelve weeks, but probably remain with their mother through the first winter, possibly until the start of the next mating period. A study mentioned by McCord and Cardoza in their account found that lynx families in the Soviet Union disbanded in their second year. The male plays no role in the raising of the young.

The biologist L. David Mech, well known for his studies of the gray wolf in Minnesota, has also studied the lynx in that area, focusing in particular on the home ranges of the species there. He found that, while the ranges of females often overlapped, those of the males did not. Male ranges were found to overlap those of females. Mech determined that male home ranges were significantly larger than female home ranges. Male home ranges varied from fifty-six to ninety-four miles. Female home ranges varied from twenty to forty-seven miles. These figures are considerably larger than figures from a study in Alaska, and suggest the size of lynx home range may be a function of the quality of habitat, as with other species.

Snowshoe hare in dark summer coat. The snowshoe hare is the primary prey of the lynx. *Jim Halfpenny*

A number of factors influence lynx mortality, ranging from the periodic collapse of its primary prey base, the snowshoe hare, to parasites and disease, trapping and hunting, loss of habitat, and predation from larger animals like wolves, bears, and larger cats. Across its range, humankind is undoubtedly one of the lynx's greatest enemies, and is constantly expanding into its once-remote winter range with new roads, oil and mineral development, and the use of snowmobiles.

CURRENT STATUS AND FUTURE RECOVERY

In 1978, the Colorado Division of Wildlife undertook a two-year verification project for the Canadian lynx which had been classified as Endangered in 1973. This study was designed to accomplish a number of goals: to ascertain the historical status of the species, to verify their current existence, to estimate current population levels, to identify key habitat, and to determine further research goals and management guidelines. It positively verified, through recent tracks, reports, and specimens, that a viable, if sparse, lynx population presently exists in certain areas of Colorado.

Similar research methods were employed to those in the wolverine verification including, in the early stages, a historical literature review, interviews with knowledgeable individuals in Colorado, the study of specimens in museums and private collections, and the distribution of over three thousand requests for information. A 1975 survey of Colorado fur trappers was studied for possible sightings. Field work focused on approximately four hundred miles of trail, which was searched for lynx tracks during the winter months using skis and snowmobiles. Those tracks greater than 3.4 inches wide with a straddle less than 7.2 inches and a stride less than 17.2 inches, but only sinking shallowly into the snow, were classified by researchers as lynx tracks. Deep snows hindered attempts by the study team to run and tree lynx with trained lion hounds.

As a result of the two-year study, Canadian lynxes were verified in eight counties of Colorado and reported without verification in ten counties. The most recent specimens from Gunnison, Summit, Conejos, and Montrose counties were taken prior to 1926, and the most recent specimens from Eagle, Pitkin, Lake, and Clear Creek counties were taken between 1969 and 1974. Those taken in the latter time period include the following: a lynx trapped southeast of Leadville (Lake County) in 1969; a lynx trapped on Guanella Pass (Clear Creek County) in 1972; and a lynx trapped near

Vail (Eagle County) in 1973–74. Additionally, since 1969 seven confirmed sets of tracks, including two lynx tracked during the verification program, have been found or reported in Pitkin, Eagle, and Lake counties.

From the study, it is apparent that lynx in Colorado, as with lynx in other regions, tend to be members of the spruce-fir/snowshoe hare association. Lynx tracks found during the study were located in or near spruce-fir forests, with large rock outcroppings nearby, and either on north-facing slopes or on the sides of narrow north-facing valleys. The present distribution of lynx in Colorado, according to the final report of the study team, is probably discontinuous and includes the following: Fryingpan River drainage upstream from Meredith in Eagle and Pitkin counties; Vail area in Eagle County, southeast of Leadville in Lake County; and the Guanella Pass-Mount Evans area of Clear Creek County. Researchers also believe, as stated in their summary, that lynx may exist in other areas of these four counties, as well as in Summit, Grand, and Park counties where spruce-fir associations occur and snowshoe hare are abundant. Finally, they observed that it appears that lynx in Colorado experience population cycles that are similar, and possibly synchronized with, those found in northern lynx populations.

Researchers concluded that: "No present or potential threats to lynx, their habitat, or their probable prey base were identified during the study. . .Management of spruce-fir stands and snowshoe hare should benefit lynx." It was also noted that the legislation designed to protect the lynx hinders information gathering because it is considered a crime to kill a lynx, even accidentally. People are naturally reluctant to report anything, given the penalties. This, of course, is a small price to pay to have a species protected from illegal trapping and hunting.

Like the wolverine, the lynx seems to offer promise for a formal recovery effort. That the lynx has been recently trapped or tracked in Colorado helps its case. There is, to many, a big difference between preservation and restoration. The lynx would fall in the former category. This would be easier to justify, in terms of committing personnel and funds. As with the wolverine, opponents argue that the lynx was never plentiful in the state and that it was a peripheral species, at the southern limit of its historic range in the Rockies. Proponents say, as with the wolverine, that the lynx clearly once lived in Colorado in greater numbers than it does today. They believe that we have an obligation, given the fact that its habitat remains intact, to help in its recovery. Further, the live trapping, radio collaring, and further monitoring of current populations, together with the study of newly released lynx, could help us understand more about this reclusive mammal.

A fully mounted lynx that was trapped by Anton Purkat in December 1969 southeast of Leadville in Lake County. Tracks at that time observed by Mr. Purkat indicated that two lynx were present in the area. *Jim Halfpenny*

The lynx in Colorado could benefit from the same methods outlined in the wolverine chapter—the formation of a "Colorado Lynx Society" or similar group, the raising of funds, and the formation of an agenda for preservation and most probably restoration. Whereas not much is known about the restoration of wolverines, there exists at least one successful lynx recovery project that has been documented. In 1976 the Yugoslavian government released three pairs of lynxes in a large forested district the species formerly occupied. With further conservation efforts, the lynx have multiplied to the extent that it is now estimated there are over one hundred of them. In 1983, three were taken legally by hunters.

Might not the same occur in Colorado? Possibly. There are several locations that immediately come to mind as being suitable for a lynx recovery project, ranging from an area where lynx are thought to currently live, such as the Holy Cross Wilderness-Hunter-Fryingpan Wilderness—Collegiate Peaks Wilderness region, to areas in which lynx could be imported and released, such as Rocky Mountain National Park or the San Juan Mountains. Again, an obvious benefit of the national park would be that there is no trapping, hunting, or grazing, all areas of possible conflict.

Not long ago I had the opportunity to examine an Alaskan lynx pelt at the University of Colorado Museum in Boulder. I was amazed at its extraordinary beauty, at the rare shades of silver, gray, brown, black, and white, and the lushness of the fur itself. I thought of the derivation of the word lynx—it comes from the Greek *leukos*, meaning white or light. That lovely light colored pelt, itself like so many variations of sun, shadow, and snow, immediately brought its light-filled high-mountain habitat to mind. To have the lynx back in Colorado in a healthy population or set of populations would be to many a worthy enterprise, and one probably not very difficult to achieve.

VII

SIDE CANYONS

THE GRIZZLY BEAR

There are lots of ways to get involved in helping to protect the grizzly bear. When you're in grizzly country, hike wisely and use the land gently. That goes beyond vacation visits, of course; if you care about grizzly bears, don't build your second home in, or otherwise tamper with, grizzly bear habitat.

— Paul Schullery, *The Bears of Yellowstone*

INTRODUCTION

We left the corral in Sunlight Basin, forty-five miles northwest of Cody, Wyoming, when the last July stars were still burning in the sky. We rode southwest along the alfalfa fields of a neighboring ranch, passed through the Forest Service gate, left the gate and the sage and the cattle and the world behind us, and entered the North Absaroka Wilderness Area. For several miles the trail paralleled the beaver ponds and dense willows of a small trout stream, running along a burned-over ridge thick with secondary growth. The trail rose gently through the lodgepole pines, and the horse's hooves were muffled by the fallen needles. Someone saw a cow moose and her spring calf browsing down by the stream, and, up higher, the coyotes were all singing before they bedded down. Gradually it became day and the birds stopped singing, and gradually we got into the aspen, the elk parks, and the open-timbered spruce-fir stands. The mule deer began to scatter and climb up toward their daybeds. After the third ridge, the old outfitter's trail disappeared completely, and we followed the trails the elk had made over the ages, sometimes spotting their shed antlers in the deep grass beside the trail, and sometimes skulls with the antlers still attached. Always we kept pushing on toward the high tundra at the head of the valley, a rolling treeless region known as Elkhorn Peak. I had been up there twice before that summer, so I knew the way.

By nine that morning we reached timberline, tied off the horses for the day, put on our day packs, laboriously climbed up a steep avalanche chute, and topped out on the saddle overlooking Dead Indian Creek to the south. Back up north the ranch looked very small in the valley, and the road could not be seen. The sun felt warm, and so we stopped to have a snack and to rest. Someone spotted a herd of elk grazing in a distant cirque and we shared a pair of binoculars. The big bulls were down in the timber, ghosting below the main herd. After ten minutes the wind was too cold to stand still, so we continued on. We had the whole afternoon to explore the headwaters of Dead Indian. The sky was very clear and blue, and it looked to some like it would not rain again, as it had all week, but I knew it would from the small line of clouds already building over Yellowstone to the west.

We were ten miles from the ranch and about twenty minutes from our lunch point, where we would turn back, when it happened. A golden eagle was climbing the light summer thermals, and a pika was chirping from a meandering rock channel. The prematurely graying attorney general of a small midwestern state was explaining the reform of tort liability law to me and I was trying to appear somewhat interested when suddenly I saw it, something dark on a vast glittering snowfield below us. It was looking up at us, over its shoulder, turning even as it saw us. Nearby I could see some places where the sod had been rolled over, where it was still wet and black. Now it was up and moving, at first slowly and then faster, its bulk flowing gracefully over the terrain, angling down toward the dark green edge of the high timber. The sun was glistening brightly on the silver guard hairs of its prominent hump. It was El Oso Plateado, Old Mose—the Great White Bear. I stopped abruptly and everyone stopped behind me.

"Look!" I turned and shouted to them, scattered behind me over the slope for a hundred yards. "What?" they called back, with confused excitement. "There!" I pointed to where a long spruce-fir stringer rose up a side ridge like a crooked finger onto the tundra. The bear was rapidly narrowing the quarter mile distance to cover. They all looked down, squinting and leaning and straining. The bear was moving fast now, gaining momentum on the incline, moving as fast as a horse trying to avoid the falling loop of a wrangler's outstretched lariat. "Where is it?" "What is it?" People turning for directions, my hand pointing steadily at the bear. "It's a grizzly bear!" "Where?" "There! Right there!" "I see it! I see it!" "Yes! There!" It was almost gone now, another forty yards. People holding their hands over their eyes. One man with binoculars, his mouth open in wonder. "My God!" he says. "What a piece of work he is!" "A grizzly bear!" "A grizzly bear!" "A grizzly bear!" Adults jumping up and down. A round of cheers. General applause.

We pushed on across the mountains that day toward the objective we had leisurely marked for ourselves, chattering excitedly as we argued over weight, sex, color, shape, confirmation, disposition, family history, and even personality. They had come from all over America, all for one moment like this, one experience real and unvarnished and unique, something to take back with them, proudly, from the western wilderness. It would be, in their memory, more priceless than a rare first edition from a Cambridge bookstore or a lost work of art from a shop in Paris. They would always treasure it and hold it dear. Lunch was eaten quickly in the lee of a small island of wind-flagged spruce, and we turned back just as the clouds began to boil in over the divide. No one minded the rain that poured down upon us an hour later as we slipped toward timberline on Elkhorn, or the early dusk that found us still on the high trails several miles above the ranch. We didn't care. We couldn't stop talking about it. The day would be one of the best days of our lives. We had seen a grizzly bear, not stuffed in a museum diorama or caged in a zoo, but out in the wild—where it belonged.

To see a living grizzly bear in Colorado today, and over most of its former range west of the Mississippi, one must go not to the most remote locations in the state but to the heart of its major city. Even on a crowded summer afternoon, one notices that the noisy throngs at the Denver Zoo become strangely silent and self absorbed, almost reverential, as they pass from the frolicking playfulness of the seal pool or the musky quiet of the primate house to the large outdoor enclosure containing the three adult specimens of *Ursus arctos horribilis*. Parents needlessly admonish children not to get too close to the edge. Children, oblivious to the warning, watch the creatures in captive fascination, and are loath to leave for the aviary, or worse, for home. Grandparents lean even farther than grandchildren across the railings, straining to glimpse something that everyone has missed before,

An adult grizzly bear in its cage at the Denver Zoo. *Susan Goldstein*

or that they will never see again. A few teenagers perhaps taunt the animals, or insolently mock their imprisonment, as if to scorn the invisible fetters with which society has begun to restrict their own natural freedom. Final pictures are taken. A few peanuts or apple slices are furtively thrown. The crowds move on, but are forever replaced.

The bears remain, day after day, year after year, as long as they live, far from the wild places in which their ancestors roamed. They have, even in the zoo, a certain dignity, a distinct quality of omnipotence, of aloofness, of extraordinary strength only at momentary rest. One finds in them the same look one finds in only a very few other animals in the world, the look of strength in repose, of untapped but unquestionable power: the look of the great white shark, the bison, the bald eagle, the elephant, the African lion. The Romantic poet John Keats, in his epic poem "Hyperion," reserved this look for the gods, for the fallen Titans. He called it the look of "supreme contempt." That is the way the grizzly bears look in the zoo, as the unlikely creatures that have replaced them stare mutely.

All of these people have seen a living relic of our recent history in the Rockies, and perhaps an omen of our future as well. All, or most, it would seem, are visibly changed by the experience. What is it that so moves and stills them? Perhaps it is the enormous hump of muscle that forms the mass of the shoulder, the machinery of an arm that can kill an elk with a single blow to the head, or lift a boulder to get at a nest of marmots. Perhaps it is the ability to rise up on its hind legs and walk like a man on soft-soled feet, a capacity that so impressed the Neanderthal, some forty thousand years ago, that they formed cults in the great bear's honor and worshipped its sun-bleached skull. Perhaps it is the impossibly small eyes that still seem to see everything, or the all-sensing nose and ears, or the brain that can plan and decide, attack or back off, organize and remember, destroy or build. Perhaps it is the ability to store fat and sleep peacefully while all the rest of the world, including humans, foolishly struggles to survive the harsh winters of the northern latitudes. Perhaps it is the rotating forearm and the ability to grasp and hold objects with its dextrous front claws almost as if they were fingers.

These bears resonate with a multitude of associations, and evoke a whole series of powerful images and dormant memories from our historic and prehistoric past. For thousands of years they lived largely unchallenged in the vast pristine wilderness of Colorado and elsewhere on the continent. They quietly went about their daily business of making a respectable living in the world: eating, digging, fishing, foraging, killing, burying, making daybeds, defending themselves, mating, raising their young, and building their dens. Then the Europeans arrived, at first with black powder muskets and pistols, then with enormous no. 6 Newhouse steel traps, and bottles of strychnine and cyanide, and, most pernicious of all, repeating rifles and revolvers. There were never as many as were thought, they were slow to reproduce and to mature, and, before anyone knew it, they were all gone. Why did this tragedy occur? Frank Craighead said it best: "The grizzly," he wrote, "is a magnificent creature whose greatest fault is that he competes with man." Humankind's intolerance for this and other of its former competitors in the natural world, has led to their decline and often their demise. The loss, while incalculable, is not irreversible. We have the ready wilderness. We have the ready stocks of wild bears. That the bear could once again dwell in the wilds of Colorado and elsewhere in its historic range has, if not been accepted, at least been seriously proposed.

A grizzled Western Slope cowboy once put it best to me, in the simple and colorful parlance of his trade: "A mountain without Old Ephraim is like a bowl of chili without the chili." Aldo Leopold put it another way, writing of these little-understood creatures that claim, at worst "a cow a year and a few square miles of useless rocks." After one of the last grizzlies in Arizona, "Big Foot" of the Escudilla, was killed by a set-gun trap in a gorge, Leopold wrote that, "Escudilla still hangs on the horizon, but when you see it you no longer think of bear. It's only a mountain now." Like the loss of the fabled Mississippi black bear in William Faulkner's masterpiece *Go Down, Moses*, the loss of the Escudilla grizzly corresponded with, and came to symbolize for Leopold, and many others, the loss of the wilderness itself. The wilderness, Faulkner wrote in his novel, was something "whose edges were being constantly and punily gnawed at by men with plows and axes who feared it because it was wilderness." The black bear of Faulkner's story was much like the grizzly bear of Leopold's Escudilla, or the last grizzly bear of New Mexico, killed on the Gila River in 1931, or one of the last grizzlies of Colorado, killed on the Navajo River on September 23, 1979:

> It loomed and towered in his dreams before he even saw the unaxed woods where it left its crooked print, shaggy, tremendous, red-eyed, not malevolent but just big, too big for the dogs which tried to ride it down, for the men and the bullets they fired into it; too big for the very country which was its constricting scope . . . not . . . a mortal beast but an anachronism indomitable and invincible out of an old, dead time, a phantom, epitome and apotheosis of the old wild life . . . the old bear, solitary, indomitable, and

Reports of grizzly bears in Colorado often turn out to be sightings of the reclusive but common black bear. The grizzly (above) may be distinguished from the black (below) by its dished face and prominent shoulder hump, and of course its generally larger size. *William Ervin (grizzly) and Charles William Murray, Jr. (black bear)*

alone; widowered, childless, and absolved of mortality—Old Priam reft of his old wife and outlived all his sons.

PAST HISTORY

The prehistoric ancestor of all present day bears, from the spectacled bear of the Andean highlands to the polar bear of the northern ice floes, was the Etruscan bear, which lived in the forests of Asia about two million years ago. During the warmer interglacial periods of the Ice Age, new bear species began to evolve from this common ancestor, bears that were adapting to the tundra vegetations that were colonizing vast areas exposed by retreating ice. These bears include the cave bear in Europe and the brown bear in Asia. The Etruscan bear was also the ancestor of both the Asiatic black bear and the American black bear. Members of this black bear line began to wander over into North America approximately 500,000 years ago, and, isolated from their ancestors, soon began to adapt to the unique resources of the continent and to evolve over the ages into the American black bear. These bears have since flourished in the divergent ecosystems available in North America, and are found in habitats as diverse as the Florida Everglades, suburban communities along the Atlantic Seaboard, the desert uplands of the Southwest, and the fringes of the High Arctic. Unlike the grizzly bear, which evolved on the tundra and the open plains, the black bear evolved in the forest and prefers the protection of forest cover, which has resulted in different, less aggressive, behavior patterns than are found in the grizzly bear.

About fifty thousand years ago, brown bears first crossed the treeless Bering Land Bridge, and began to spread southward into North America. Two subspecies of brown bear now occupy the continent: the grizzly bear (*Ursus arctos horribilis*) of interior and mountain regions, and the brown bear (*Ursus arctos middendorffi*), found on the salmon-rich islands of Kodiak, Shuyak, and Afognak, as well as other coastal regions of southern Alaska. For brown bears to successfully adapt to these new post-glacial habitats, their forest adaptations had to be significantly modified. Far from the safety of the dense Asian and European forests, both morphological and behavioral changes were necessary in order that the new bears might protect themselves and their vulnerable young from the host of Pleistocene carnivores. The most obvious behavioral adaptation to this open, treeless environment is one that has given the grizzly bear its Latin appellation *horribilis*, the characteristic of displaying greater aggressiveness than other bears.

The historic range of the brown bear included, in Europe, almost the entire continent, from the deciduous forests of the south to the coniferous forests, taiga, and tundra of the north. About fifteen small local populations persist in Europe in such areas as the Pyrenees Mountains of Spain, the Apennine Mountains of Italy, in parts of Czechoslovakia and Rumania (Carpathian Mountains), northern Greece, and in Norway. Some of these populations are nearly extinct, such as those on the French/Spanish border, while others are surprisingly abundant, such as those in Poland, Yugoslavia, and Hungary. The brown bear is still quite numerous in the USSR, but is subjected to growing habitat loss and hunting pressure there. The North African subspecies was exterminated approximately one hundred years ago.

In North America, the bear was originally found from Ontario westward to the Pacific Coast, and south into Texas and the Sierra Madre of Mexico. As the forces of American growth pushed the population westward, the grizzly bear population rapidly diminished from an estimated high of one hundred thousand in 1800 to fewer than one thousand bears at present. Habitat deterioration, predator control, commercial trapping, sport hunting, and protection of human life were all leading causes of this sudden diminution. Grizzly bears disappeared from Texas about 1890 and from California by 1922. Those in the Dakotas, Nebraska, Kansas, and elsewhere on the plains had vanished long before that. The last known grizzly bear in Utah was killed in 1923, in Oregon in 1931, in New Mexico in 1931, and in Arizona in 1935. By 1970 only a handful of populations were left, inhabiting the Greater Yellowstone Ecosystem, the northern Continental Divide in Montana, the Selway-Bitterroot Wilderness Area in Idaho, the North Cascades of Washington, the Selkirks of Idaho, and the Cabinet Mountains of Montana. Grizzly bears are considered marginal in some of these areas, such as the North Cascades, the Selkirks, and the Selway-Bitterroot Wilderness Area. The Sierra del Nido of Sonora, and the Sierra watershed of the Rio Yanqui in Chihuahua may hold relic populations, as might the San Juan Mountains of Colorado, but without new members all three (if in fact they exist), will gradually become extinct because of the effects of inbreeding and man-caused mortality. Grizzly bear populations in Alaska and in Canada (Alberta, British Columbia, Northwest Territories, and the Yukon) are not currently considered to be threatened or endangered.

The Spanish explorer Coronado was probably the first European to see a grizzly in the New World as he traveled up the Rio Grande Valley in 1540 through what is now the state of New Mexico. In 1602 another Spaniard, Sebastian Viscaino, described grizzlies feeding upon the carcass of a whale near Monterey, California. The first reference to a grizzly bear in the journals of an Englishman occurs in a diary kept by Henry Kelsey, a young man sent by the Hudson's Bay Company to explore the prairie provinces:

> (August 20, 1691) To day we pitcht to y(e) outtermost Edge of y(e) woods this plain affords Nothing but short Round sticky grass & Buffillo & a great sor(t) of a Bear w(hich) is Bigger then any white [polar] Bear & is Neither White nor Black But silver hair'd like our English Rabbit . . .

Later Kelsey relates that, after killing a grizzly bear, he found the meat good but was discouraged from keeping the hide of the bear by the Indians because "they said it was God."

Little more is found in chronicles about the grizzly bear until 1805, when President Jefferson commissioned captains Meriwether Lewis and William Clark to explore the Missouri drainage and find a route to the Pacific Ocean. They were also directed to seek out and collect specimens of the flora and fauna and duly returned from the West with many items, including the pelt of a grizzly bear. Their journals contain repeated references to a great bear, commonly designated as the brown, white, or variegated bear. One of their first encounters occurred on Monday, April 29, 1805, while still along the Missouri River (from Lewis's journal):

> Set out this morning at the usual hour; the wind was moderate; I walked on shore with one man. about 8 A.M. we fell in with two brown or yellow (white) bear; both of which we wounded . . . this animal appeared to me to differ from the black bear; it is a much more furious and formidable animal, and will frequently pursue the hunter. It is astonishing to see the wounds they will bear before they can be put to death. The Indians may well fear this animal as they generally are with their bows and arrows or indifferent fuzees, but in the hands of skillful riflemen they are by no means as formidable or dangerous as they have been represented.

The reference to the firepower advantage of the musket and pistol is both ominous and prophetic. It would be just these sorts of weapons that, together with traps, poisons, and multiple firing mechanisms, would eventually devastate the species. Also informative is the reference to the extraordinary ability of the animal to tolerate and survive serious wounds due to its hard muscular structure, its acidic body tissue, and its unique vascular system with an unusually large heart and thick-walled aorta. The specimen obtained on this trip was used by George Ord of Philadelphia in 1815 as the basis for the scientific name he gave to the species (*Ursus horribilis*). *Ursus arctos* was the name given to the European brown bear by the taxonomist Linnaeus in the eighteenth century. The species was recognized as being Holarctic as early as 1851 by the naturalist von Middendorf.

During the same period as the Lewis and Clark expedition, President Jefferson ordered another army officer, Zebulon Montgomery Pike, to explore the southern portions of the land he acquired from France in 1803 through the Louisiana Purchase. For two years Pike wandered through the vast territory, reaching the Front Range of the Rocky Mountains in Colorado and traveling southward to Santa Fe and down the Rio Grande, eventually concluding his expedition in New Orleans. It was Pike who returned from the West with the first live specimens of the grizzly bear. He had them placed in a museum, or zoo, in Philadelphia, where they were put on public display. So taken was Jefferson by this new species that he wrote Pike a letter inquiring where they had been collected and any other particulars of their captivity. Pike responded on February 3, 1808:

> Sir: I had the honor of receiving your note last evening . . . The Bears were taken by an Indian in the mountain which divides the western branch of the Rio del Norte [Rio Grande] and some small rivers, which discharged their waters into the east side of the Gulf of California, near the dividing line between the provinces of Biscay and Sonora . . . Although then more than 1600 miles from our frontier post, Natchitoches, I purchased them of the savage, and for three or four days made my men carry them in their laps on horseback. As they would eat nothing but milk, they were in danger of starving. I then had a cage prepared for both, which was carried on a mule, lashed between two packs, but always ordered them to be let out the moment we halted, and not shut up again until we were prepared to march. By this treatment they became exceedingly docile when at liberty, following my men, whom they learned to distinguish from the Spanish dragoons, by their feeding them, and encamping with them, like dogs through out camps . . . they would play like young puppies with each other and the soldiers . . . They will be one year old on the first of next month, March, 1808 — and, as I am informed, they frequently arrive at the weight of eight hundred pounds. . . . they seldom or never attack a man unprovoked, but defend themselves courageously . . .

These two bears, so friendly in their youth, were eventually killed in the zoo after they pulled a monkey between the bars of their cage, and devoured it on the spot.

The first reference to a grizzly bear in Colorado occurs in the journals of Thomas Say, a noted naturalist of the period, who accompanied Major Stephen Harriman Long on his expedition across the plains to the Front Range of Colorado. Though more than 150 years old, Say's 1820 description is still remarkably accurate and useful:

It may with certainty be distinguished from all known species of this genus by its elongated claws, and the rectinlinear [sic] or slightly arched figure of its facial profile. . . . On the front of the Grizzly Bear the hair is short, and between the anterior to the eyes it is very much so. On the rest of the body, it is long and very thickly set, being black and coarser on the legs, feet, shoulders, throat, behind the thighs, and beneath the belly. On the snout it is paler. The ears are short and rounded, the forehead somewhat convex, or arcuated; and the line of the profile continuous on the snout, without any indentations between the eyes . . . The eyes are quite small . . . The iris is of a light reddish-brown or burnt sienna color. The muffle of the nostrils is black . . . The lips are capable of being extended anteriorly, especially the upper one . . . The color of the Grizzly Bear varies very considerably, according to age and its particular state of pelage . . . Hence they have been described as brown, white, variegated, by Lewis and Clark although evidently of the same species judging by all other characteristics; in advanced life the colour is that peculiar mixture of white, brown, and black, which has procured for the bear the appropriate name "grizzly."

The year after Long and his expedition returned on November 13, 1821, Lewis Dawson, a member of the Fowler expedition from Ft. Smith, Arkansas to Santa Fe, New Mexico, was killed by a grizzly bear in Colorado near the Purgatoire River. He was the first white man known to be killed by a grizzly in the state. It is also possible, as a note, that Dawson was the first American citizen to die and be buried in Colorado. In any event, the "100 Year War" between the white man and the grizzly bear had formally begun in Colorado, with the bear apparently winning the first battle.

Two years after Dawson's death, the famous explorer/writer James Ohio Pattie entered Colorado along the Arkansas River and passed south over Raton Pass en route to Taos and Santa Fe. Pattie relates in his journal that the Pawnees of eastern Colorado, like many of the western tribes, highly coveted the long white front claws of the grizzly bear, and that the bears were plentiful on the High Plains. September 9, 1823:

The succeeding morning we crossed the ridge, and came to water in the evening where we encamped. Here we killed a white bear, which occupied

several of us at least an hour. It was constantly in chase of one or another
of us, thus withholding us from shooting at it, through fear of wounding
each other. This was the first I had ever seen. His claws were four inches
long, and very sharp. He had killed a buffalo bull, eaten a part of it, and
buried the remainder. When we came upon him he was watching the spot,
where he had buried it, to keep off the wolves, which literally surrounded
him. On the 11th . . . we killed three white bears, the claws of which I saved,
they being of considerable value among the Indians, who wear them around
the neck, as the distinguishing mark of a brave. Those Indians, who wear
this ornament, view those, who do not, as their inferiors.

Pattie had, by this account, unconsciously evened the score in the battle
between the white man and the grizzly bear. The apparent ease with which
he dispatched three more bears on September 11, simply to acquire their
claws to trade with the Indians, suggests that from this point forward there
would really be no contest between a man with a good center-bore rifle
and a grizzly bear. Twenty years later, in the journals of one of the last
of the Taos trappers, William Drannen, one finds the same sort of passage:
Colorado grizzlies killed simply because they were there, or seemed to pose
a threat, or for the sport of it, or merely to eat small portions and leave
the rest to rot.

    With the discovery of gold and silver in the Front Range there was
a massive influx of emigrants into the Colorado Territory. As the land became settled under the Homestead Act and ranching developed as the corner-
stone of the local economy, associations of cattlemen and sheep ranchers
began to offer bounties for wolves, coyotes, lions, and bears, both black
and grizzly. Only the mountain lion, black bear, and coyote survived this
period of mass extermination and persist in good numbers throughout the
state today. The destruction of wolves and of grizzly bears was seen by these
early woolgrowers and stockmen as absolutely necessary to maintain their
businesses on a profitable basis. Logging and recreational development of
the period also added to man-induced mortality of grizzly bears in Colorado. Grizzly bears were routinely destroyed except for a two-year period
between 1867 and 1869 when the Colorado Territorial Assembly briefly
established a closed season on them. Conflicts between bears and livestock
were common in this great "Age of Ranching" in Colorado, both because
of the grizzly's opportunistic feeding habits, and because ranchers had in-
vaded virtually all of the remote summer habitats used by the grizzly bears
for tens of thousands of years. By 1897, the grizzly bear had begun to be

reported as rare in Colorado. In 1905, while hunting black bears near Glenwood Springs, President Roosevelt noted that the grizzly bear was rare in Colorado. In 1915, bowing to pressure from stockmen whose industry had, for complex reasons, begun to collapse, the federal government began an extensive campaign to eliminate the grizzly bear in Colorado. By 1930, the grizzly bear was all but gone in southern Colorado, with the last grizzly in the northern part of the state reported near Rocky Mountain National Park by nature writer Enos Mills in 1920.

A few of these last grizzly bears have lingered on in the folklore and legends of Colorado, including "Old Four Toes," killed near Montrose in 1903; "Old Clubfoot," killed near Delta on October 24, 1902, who ranged from the heads of Sapinero and Curecanti creeks on the south to the North Fork of the Gunnison River on the north; "Big-foot Mary," killed south of Grand Junction in October, 1925, whose hide measured 8.5 feet and whose carcass produced 166 pounds of lard; and "Old Silver," said to have covered the White River Country now known as the Flattops Wilderness Area, who simply disappeared one day, never to be seen again. Like Old Ephraim of Utah's Wasatch Mountains or the Escudilla Grizzly of Aldo Leopold's essay or the great black bear of Faulkner's mythical Yoknapatawpha County, each of these bears was cherished in regional memory as a symbol for the wilderness, an individual whose departure was more than just the loss of an animal, but the loss of a whole frontier.

Probably the most famous of these now legendary grizzly bears of Colorado, a bear known not only in Colorado, but around the nation, was "Old Mose," an enormous boar that lived in the southeastern part of the Rockies. In his lifetime he is reputed to have killed at least two, and possibly three men (though grizzlies at this time were often blamed for the deaths of those who might have disappeared for other reasons), as well as to have taken a heavy toll of sheep and cattle. His home range was centered northwest of Canon City, around Black and Thirty-Nine Mile mountains, and he is said to have been seen and tracked for over thirty-five years in this region, which is not entirely impossible given the longevity of grizzly bears. He was killed on Black Mountain, in Park County, shortly after he left his den on April 30, 1904, by James W. Anthony. He reportedly measured ten feet four inches from nose to tail, and nine feet six inches around the middle. His body weight, with the viscera removed, was nine hundred pounds, and his live fall weight was estimated to be around twelve hundred pounds. The skull measured fifteen inches from front to rear, and was fourteen inches wide. To put this in perspective, the world record Kodiak bear

(Boone and Crockett Records, 1977, 7th Edition) measures 17 feet 15/16 inches by 12 feet 13/16 inches, and the world record grizzly bear measures 17 feet 6/16 inches by 9 feet 12/16 inches. Old Mose was a big grizzly bear, particularly when his habitat is compared with richer environments farther north in Alaska, and also keeping in mind Bergman's rule that the size of animals within a group is smallest in the south and largest in the north. If the tales are true, his penchant for range-fattened cattle and sheep could have contributed to this extraordinary size, but genetics also was no doubt important. Dr. E. G. Lancaster, then Chairman of the Department of Biology at Colorado College in Colorado Springs, studied the brain of Old Mose and published an article on his study in *Outdoor Life* magazine. The brain weighed fifteen ounces, just a tiny fraction of the gross body weight. This is about the weight of the brain of a normal newborn human baby. The centers of smelling and hearing were, he reported, enormously developed. The optic nerve was small, and the optic regions at the rear of the brain were poorly developed. He also noted that the brain was wide across the areas controlling motor activity.

The last grizzly bear to develop a local reputation was the bear killed on Lone Cone Mountain in San Miguel County on May 26, 1907. Merritt Cary, who measured the skin of this bear, gave the following measurements. Like all such records, they are probably exaggerated by stretching. The distance between tips of foreclaws, outstretched, was 66.5 inches. The length from the tip of the tail to the end of the nose was eighty-seven inches. The longest foreclaw was 4.5 inches. The hind claws were all badly worn and under one inch in length. Cary believed the advanced age of this bear was indicated by the worn teeth and hind claws. The following description of the pelt is given:

> The pelt was in prime condition, with a uniformly short, dense pelage, shortest on the back between the shoulders, where the hair averaged about 3-1/8 inches in length, and longest on the sides of the upper fore legs, where it averaged 6-1/4 inches. The Indian (one of the men who killed it) aptly likened the flaps of long shaggy hair to a cowboy's chaps, and said the resemblance in life was most striking. The fur was a dark, rich clove brown at base throughout, shading into plain brownish black on sides and on fore and hind legs; ear and face dark brown; nose clay brown; dorsal area, from rump to between ears, a beautiful silvery clove brown, brightest between shoulders, owing to greater length of silvered area at tip of hairs.

After the demise of these last great legends, reports of grizzly bears in

Colorado began to dwindle. Some reports after this period no doubt confused the yellow or cinnamon phase of the black bear with the grizzly. As early as 1906, Edward Warren had noted that "one often hears of Grizzly Bears being killed [in Colorado], but they almost always turn out to be some form of the Black Bear." What few grizzly bears remained in Colorado seemed to be found exclusively in the most remote portions of the San Juan Mountains. Over the next fifty years, a few grizzlies were killed in this area. In 1913, between April 18 and May 5, three grizzlies were trapped on the lower Navajo River by William Weissel. In 1930, exact date unknown, a grizzly was reported killed on Lone Cone Peak in southwestern Colorado. At least five grizzlies were reportedly taken in southwestern Colorado from 1948 through 1950. In August 1951, sheepherder Al Lobato killed a young blond-phased grizzly bear near Blue Lake in the south San Juans. The head and claws, prepared by taxidermist Ernie Wilkinson of Monte Vista, Colorado, are on display at the Skyline Lodge in Platoro.

On September 5, 1951, Ernie Wilkinson (who also worked as a government trapper at the time) trapped a two- or three-year-old male grizzly in Starvation Gulch, near the headwaters of the Rio Grande River in the San Juan Mountains. I interviewed Ernie Wilkinson in Monte Vista on August 14, 1986 about the incident. Ernie was born on July 20, 1924 in Monte Vista and has lived in the San Luis Valley all his life, supporting himself as a trapper, taxidermist, guide, wildlife photographer, and lately as a nature group leader. He is the author of many outdoor articles and a recent book on winter camping. During the summer of 1951 he was responsible for predator control for fifty-three sheep camps running west from Wagon Wheel Gap up to Stoney Pass. In late August of that year he received a report of bear problems in Starvation Gulch, where about twelve hundred head of sheep were being grazed.

When he arrived in Starvation Gulch, Ernie found several dead sheep. Despite working in the high mountains for a number of years, Ernie had never seen a grizzly or any grizzly sign. He naturally suspected a black bear was the culprit. Just at timberline he built a V-shaped bear cubby with a little roof at the apex and a dead sheep stuffed in underneath. The trap, a plain no. 5 open-jawed steel trap, was placed in the wide-angled entrance and chained to a nearby live tree. When he returned on September 5, expecting to find a black bear, he was surprised to discover a grizzly bear dead and over on its back near the entrance of the cubby. Having lain in the sun for several days, the carcass was beginning to decompose, and the hair was already starting to fall out. The only salvageable portion of the bear

Sheepherder Al Lobato killed this young grizzly bear at Blue Lake in the South San Juan area in August 1951. It can be seen at the Skyline Lodge in Platoro, Colorado, and is held here by Mr. Jim Weaver of Wyandote, Oklahoma, head wrangler and hunting guide at the lodge. *John Murray*

was its right front forepaw, which was sticking up in the air away from the body. Ernie cut this off and has saved it ever since. When he returned to the site during elk season, scavengers had scattered the skull and carcass and nothing could be found. That was the first and only grizzly Ernie has seen in the San Juans.

The next season Lloyd Anderson of Pagosa Springs, who worked as a government trapper on the San Juan National Forest side of the Continental Divide, trapped a grizzly bear near the headwaters of the Los Pinos River. It is reported that two cubs escaped. This grizzly, killed in September 1952, was the last confirmed killing of a grizzly in Colorado until 1979. There is an unconfirmed report that a grizzly was taken in Saguache County in 1954. In the intervening years between 1952 and 1979 there were about ten sightings or reports of sign in the San Juans that could have been grizzlies. These include visual sightings, tracks, a skull, and incidents in which horse carcasses were moved large distances. In 1954, authorities created the Rio Grande-San Juan Grizzly Bear Management Act, in hopes of preserving the last few grizzlies, and made the killing of them illegal throughout the state. It was, however, too little too late. The grizzly bear was gone, extirpated in the state and over the Southwest except for a few last bears in the Sierra Madres and Sierra del Nido of northern Mexico. It had been persecuted for over one hundred years, and the cumulative effects of cyanide, strychnine, Compound 1080, set-gun traps, steel traps, and repeating rifles had finally taken their toll. The grizzly bear no longer lived in Colorado. Or so everyone thought for the next twenty-seven years.

NATURAL HISTORY

The grizzly bear first became the object of serious scientific inquiry in the early part of the twentieth century. Pioneer naturalists such as William Wright of the Northern Rockies and Enos Mills of Colorado began to spend considerable time in the field observing grizzly bears and attempting to learn something about their lifestyle. Their writings and conclusions, while crude by modern standards, represent the first concrete steps to acquire useful scientific knowledge about the habits and habitats of this reclusive and secretive mammal. The next quantum leap occurred in Alaska, when the venerated naturalist Adolph Murie spent a total of twenty-two summers in Denali National Park (then Mt. McKinley National Park) between 1922 and 1944 studying both the grizzly bear and the Alaskan wolf. By carefully following individual bears and bear families, by studying their scats, noting their food requirements, observing their denning locations, and delineating their home ranges, social structure, population dynamics, and relationships with other animals, Murie helped to lay the foundation for the modern science of grizzly bear ecology. His book *The Grizzlies of Mount McKinley*, is now considered a classic in the literature of the grizzly bear. "Wild grizzlies," Murie wrote ". . . conducting their affairs undisturbed, are the essence of wilderness spirit."

Some of the most comprehensive information on the natural history of the grizzly bear comes from the study of John and Frank Craighead in Yellowstone National Park that began in the summer of 1959 and continued through 1971. The length and depth of their investigation, as well as the exacting and often innovative methods they employed, have made it, and the data it produced, legendary. The Craigheads developed such techniques as radio-tracking collars, biotelemetry, and satellite telemetry. Their probing research project concluded in 1971 when, after a series of disagreements with the National Park Service over management issues, the brothers parted company with the park. Frank eventually retired. John began a lengthy study in the Lincoln-Scapegoat Wilderness Area of northern Montana in which he developed vegetative mapping techniques through the use of LAND-SAT satellite images. He is currently conducting similar research in the Gates of the Arctic National Park in the Brooks Range of northern Alaska. The two brothers have helped to bring the science of grizzly bear ecology into the space age, and will no doubt be long remembered for their many contributions in this area. Also, they brought the Yellowstone grizzly to national attention through their writings and their National Geographic television special. As Frank Craighead wrote in his popular book *Track of the Grizzly*:

> Alive, the grizzly is a symbol of freedom and understanding—a sign that man *can* learn to conserve what is left of the earth . . . In its beleaguered condition, it is above all a symbol of what man is doing to the entire planet. If we can learn from these experiences, and learn rationally, both the grizzly and man may have a chance to survive.

Many other dedicated scientists have now followed the path blazed by these pioneers, including Charles Jonkel, Richard Knight, and Cliff Martinka in the lower forty-eight states; A. A. Kistchinski, who studied brown bears in Siberia and Kamchatka; and A. M. Pearson, who has studied the barren grounds grizzly bear in the Yukon Territory. As a result of this unprecedented amount of study much is known about the grizzly bear, but much still needs to be learned. One needs only to look at the current decline of the Yellowstone grizzly bear population, which has alarmed, divided, and mystified the scientific community, to realize that our ignorance about the species still surpasses our knowledge. It is to be hoped that we will learn more about the secret of how to help them survive before it is too late.

In the field the grizzly bear may be distinguished most easily from the black bear by the pronounced shoulder hump, although this feature is sometimes complicated by body posturing. Also, the hump is often not noticeable in younger grizzlies. Pelage is also quite different. Grizzly pelts are often silver tipped with white-tipped guard hairs from 2.5 to 5 inches in length. Their coats are various colors, including claybank, jet black, honey, sandy, mud brown, and even blond. They sometimes have white throat collars and dark eye patches, or pale markings on their sides. The facial profile of the grizzly, unlike that of the black bear, is somewhat concave or dished, with the forehead rising from the muzzle and showing a break in the line of the face. The foreclaws, also unlike those of the black bear, are quite long, up to four inches, are sometimes cream colored, and often visible at great distance. These claws make it impossible for most adult grizzlies to climb trees although, standing on their hind legs and extending their front paws, they can reach up to eight or ten feet.

An occasional male may exceed one thousand pounds, but most weigh, at maturity, between five hundred and six hundred pounds. Females are generally smaller, in the three-hundred- to four-hundred-pound range. Adults stand 3.5 to 4.5 feet at the hump when on all fours. Either sex can run in excess of twenty-five miles per hour for short distances. Grizzly bears are long-lived mammals, with the oldest captive bear living forty-seven years. A. M. Pearson listed the oldest ages in his study as twenty-eight years for males and twenty-three years for females. Craighead and Knight both found the oldest age for grizzlies in Yellowstone to be 25.5 years.

Grizzly bear sign most commonly found in the wild includes tracks, scats, large digs, rubbing areas, daybeds, and excavated dens. Because of their foreclaws, grizzly bear tracks are easily distinguished from those of black bears, with the claw marks extending approximately three inches in front of the toe prints of the front paws. Also on the front tracks, the junction of the toes with the main pad forms a straighter line than with the black bear. The appearance of the grizzly bear track is both more square and significantly larger than that of a black bear. A grizzly bear tracked near Victorio Lake in the San Juan Mountains in the 1960s had a hind track

that was slightly less than a foot in length. Grizzly bear scats are also larger
than those of black bears. Formed droppings greater than two inches in
diameter or more than 2.5 quarts in volume are usually considered to have
been made by an adult grizzly. Grizzly bears ingest hair while grooming
themselves, and these hairs can be studied to determine species.

A familiar sign of grizzly bear activity are digs, in which turf and rocks
are laid back or thrown aside as the bear excavates for roots, bulbs, tubers,
field mice, pocket gophers, marmots, and squirrel nut caches. A typical grizzly
bear dig is very large and deep, more so than with a black bear. Clumps
of sod as much as a foot or two in diameter are laid back. Sometimes
enormous rocks are pulled back and rolled aside. These are often seen in
wet meadows, along streams, near springs or seeps, in sidehill parks, or out
on the tundra. Sometimes associated with these microhabitats, or localized
feeding zones, are rub areas and daybeds. Rub areas, generally found near
early to midsummer habitats, are places in which the bears attempt to rub
off their shedding coats from the previous winter. Daybeds are sometimes
deeply dug and lined with boughs, moss, and grass. Root-filled scats may
be scattered nearby. Grizzly bear dens are significantly different from those
of black bears. Where black bears prefer natural rock shelters, caves, and
dead trees, grizzly bears undertake a substantial excavation often, in Yellowstone and the northern Rockies, dug between the massive roots of a large
Engelmann spruce tree.

The breeding season extends from mid-May to mid-July, with the peak
usually around the solstice in June. Throughout this period, males may
wander widely in search of receptive females. A male attends one or more
females for one to three weeks. Initially, females are intolerant of males,
but later become more accepting and permit mating to occur. Estrus can
last from a few days to over a month. Females in estrus are receptive to
practically all adult males. A male may isolate and defend a female in areas
of low bear density, but, in areas of high density, both sexes are receptive
to other partners. Litter sizes range from one to four, with the mean about
two. The Craigheads determined average sexual maturity to occur at 4.5
years, with the minimum breeding interval for females to be three to four
years. The oldest known female to conceive in Yellowstone was 22.5 years
of age. This limited reproductive capacity makes it difficult for grizzly populations, unlike those of other predators, such as mountain lions, coyotes,
and even wolves, to sustain mortality. In fact, they have one of the lowest
reproductive rates among terrestrial mammals, resulting from the late age
of first reproduction, small average litter size, and long interval between

A female Alaska brown bear and four cubs. The photographer reports that the curious thing about this picture is that the sow seen here is not the mother of these cubs. Her cubs are off to the right, and the natural mother is out of the picture. *William Ervin*

litters. This undoubtedly contributed to their rapid decline in Colorado and elsewhere in the Southwest. The Craigheads concluded that a single female is extremely fortunate, even given a longer than average lifetime, to add one breeding-age female to the local population. Consequently, the loss of even a few females every year can, over a relatively short period, lead to the possible collapse of the entire population, as could become the case in Yellowstone.

The time from conception to birth is between 229 and 266 days, with a delay in blastocyst implantation postponing embryonic development until late November or December. Birth occurs around the first of February. The cubs are initially quite small and helpless, and nurse upon the mother as she continues to sleep. They normally stay with her for approximately two and a half years, at which time the mother aggressively breaks up the family and goes off on her own, perhaps to mate that summer or the next. It is assumed, but not known for certain, that these subadults disperse beyond their mother's home range, moving directly to avoid the home ranges of other established adults. This activity increases their vulnerability and makes them susceptible to mortality, particularly that induced by man. Females apparently disperse less widely than males, and sometimes establish a home range quite near that of their mothers.

The home range of a grizzly bear must contain all of the requirements for life: "food, cover, and water, for both sexes, for all age classes, and for all seasons and activities." Areas of great value to grizzly bears include those microsites or microhabitats in which high-quality food is found, including old burns, talus slopes, wet meadows, stream bottoms, herb lands, avalanche chutes, ridge tops, sidehill parks, pond edges, springs, and seeps. Other areas of high value include forests with herb understories, fruiting shrubs, pine nuts, and starchy rooted forbs, as well as ungulate winter range where carcasses can be found under the retreating snowbanks in the spring.

An important component of the home range, it has been found, is the availability of cover. Cover is defined by grizzly bear authorities as "vege-tation and/or topography which hides 90 per cent of a grizzly from the view of a person 400 feet away. Cover should have a least diameter of 300 feet or greater." One study in Yellowstone found that most bears observed in the open were less than fifty yards from cover, and most were less than fifteen yards from cover. Whether this is an innate preference or a learned avoidance behavior is not known. The search for food is an influence on grizzly bear movement, and impels them to remain active throughout the spring, summer, and autumn, always motivated by the need to consume enough food to safely hibernate through the winter and then survive the first lean weeks of the following spring.

Adult grizzly bears are, like adult human beings, very much individu-als, but certain common characteristics have been observed. Normally they are solitary wanderers, preferring to keep to themselves in the most remote regions, far from man and from other bears. Isolated cases of social behavior have been noted, primarily among newly weaned siblings, vulnerable sub-adults, and females with offspring. While there is no evidence that grizzly bears exhibit territoriality, a solitary bear, according to one source, "appears to maintain a spacing between itself and other bears." Females with cubs may enforce a distance of one hundred yards. Bears seem to space them-selves and to limit density to conform with the carrying capacity of the ecosystem and its constituent regions. Because they are not territorial, home ranges overlap extensively, with the home ranges of adult males generally two to four times larger than that of females. These home ranges are thought to be simply too large to defend. The density of grizzly bear populations apparently is a function of the richness of the environment they inhabit, with the extremes being .62 square miles per bear on Kodiak Island and 57.9 square miles per bear in the Upper Kolyma Basin of Siberia.

The Craigheads found that the average age composition of the Yellowstone grizzly bear population during their study period was as follows: 18.6 per cent cubs, 13 per cent yearling, 24.9 per cent subadults (two to four years old), and 43.7 per cent adults. These figures have changed slightly in more recent studies.

Of all these classes, the most dangerous is the adult female with cubs. Although adult females with young comprise less than twenty per cent of the total grizzly bear population, they were found by one researcher to have caused at least seventy-nine per cent of the injuries to people during the period studied. A bear of this sort exhibits an almost reflexive response to any surprise intrusion, with surprise being the operative word. Given the opportunity, most grizzly bears will gladly give human beings a wide berth. Pursuit or defense of a food source is another common cause of man-bear incidents, particularly when outfitters are sloppy with camp supplies such as concentrated food pellets, or when backpackers do not follow wilderness guidelines. Grizzly bears will also actively defend a food source, as was seen earlier in the narrative in the passage from James O. Pattie.

Grizzly bears, being omnivorous, are extremely adaptive and flexible in their food habits, and can live on anything from maggots to acorns, moose meat to ground squirrels, wild strawberries to onion grass. In some areas they may be almost entirely herbivorous. Herbaceous plants are usually eaten just after they appear in the spring, when crude protein levels in the leaves and stalks are at their highest. These levels decline rapidly as the plants mature, and the bears turn to other protein sources, following plant phenology back to the higher elevations in which they denned. Morphological adaptations to their diet and lifestyle include large crushing molars and the greatest intestinal length relative to body length of any carnivore. Primary foods throughout the summer include corms and roots, pine nuts, rodents, grass, forbs, sedges, berries, mushrooms, and carrion. Some predation of weak ungulates occurs in both the spring and the fall.

Grizzly bears den when a combination of environmental factors alert them to the approach of winter, including decreasing day length, lower ambient air temperatures, deepening snows, and the growing unavailability of food. Apparently in most cases a point is reached when the cost of remaining active begins to exceed the benefits derived from food intake. The digging of dens is probably instinctive, beginning as early as September and as late as November. Dens are usually dug on steep slopes where wind and topography cause a deep accumulation of snow, and where snow is unlikely to melt during warm periods in the winter. These dens are usually excavated at higher elevations, well away from any human activities. Prior to entering the den, grizzly bears enter a state of extreme prehibernation lethargy, and nap at or near their den sites.

The causes of natural mortality among wild grizzly bear populations are not well known. Adult males do kill juveniles, and adults sometimes kill or severely injure other adults. Parasites and disease do not appear to be significant causes of mortality. Some bears may die in the den or shortly after emerging in the spring. Vulnerable periods in the yearly life of the grizzly include the postdenning period and stressful times during the summer or autumn when weather conditions, such as drought, adversely affect the availability of food. Man-related mortality is the major cause of grizzly bear deaths throughout their present range. As more and more essential habitat is lost or attentuated by the presence of man, whether through logging roads, mineral exploration, powerline corridors, or recreational use, the future for the species becomes more and more tenuous.

CURRENT STATUS AND FUTURE RECOVERY

The grizzly bear killed by government trapper Lloyd Anderson in 1952 was, for over a quarter of a century, thought to have been the last grizzly in Colorado. Although numerous sightings were reported to the State Division of Wildlife in this period, most were of doubtful veracity. A few, like those by Lloyd Anderson (sightings made in the San Juan Mountains in 1957, 1962, 1965, and 1967), and those by residents of the Tierra Amarilla Land Grant, were considered reliable and given careful attention. Despite several official investigations (CSU graduate student Gary Sheldon, 1955; DOW employee Gene Basset, 1965; DOW 1970–1973), no definitive empirical proof could be found of their existence, only circumstantial evidence. The grizzly bear in Colorado had become the stuff of legend, existing more around wilderness campfires and Western Slope bar stools than in reality. Although the hunting of grizzly bears remained illegal after 1954, when the special Rio Grande-San Juan Grizzly Bear Management Area was created, the project was dissolved in 1964. It seemed there were no bears left to manage, or so everyone thought.

As a tribute to the grizzly bear's tenacity however, and its amazing ability to avoid man when it wants to, we now know that at least one grizzly bear persisted after this time. Just when the world had completely forgotten about the grizzly in Colorado, on a quiet autumn evening fifty miles from nowhere, a grizzly bear, like Lazarus, rose from the dead. The story has been told many times before. A prominent Colorado big-game outfitter, forty-six-year-old Ed Wiseman of Crestone, was guiding Mike Niederee of Great Bend, Kansas, on an archery elk hunt in the region of Platoro Reservoir, in the south San Juans. On the date of the incident, September 23, 1979, at around five in the evening, Niederee reportedly jumped the bear in its daybed at a distance of ten to twenty yards. The bear, despite being surprised at close distance, chose to avoid a confrontation and fled the scene. Several hundred yards away, however, it ran into Wiseman and that is when, according to the story, the trouble began.

The bear apparently knocked Wiseman down and began to bite and maul him about the right shoulder and legs. Wiseman, an experienced outdoorsman, knew that the best thing to do when attacked is to remain passive and appear dead. This apparently did not work, so Wiseman, growing desperate, grabbed one of his hunting arrows and began stabbing the bear in the throat and neck, achieving a penetration in at least two thrusts. The bear, weakened by loss of blood and shock, released Wiseman, went off a short distance, and died. Niederee, the son of a surgeon, heard Wiseman's shouts and arrived on the scene at this time. After applying first aid, he departed to get their horses, which had been left about one and a half miles behind, and returned with them as quickly as he could. Wiseman was, however, in such bad shape that he could not complete the trip, and was left by Niederee near a large fire, with plenty of kindling. Niederee continued on to the base camp to get assistance.

Unfortunately, the incident occurred in one of the most remote places in Colorado, just over the Continental Divide from Blue Lake (elevation 11,643 feet) at the headwaters of the East Fork of the Navajo River. The trailhead, located back over the Divide at Platoro Reservoir (itself an extremely remote location), was approximately eight miles on a very rugged trail from the site of the encounter. Arriving at the base camp sometime later, Niederee told the hunting party what had happened. The camp cook immediately saddled up and rode out to the trailhead for assistance. The rest of the party, including Niederee's surgeon father, rode their horses back to Wiseman, reaching him at about 4:00 A.M. on the morning of September 24. They rebuilt his fire, which had dwindled as his condition had worsened, supplied him with fluids to counter the blood loss, and tried to keep him as comfortable as possible. Meanwhile, the camp cook had successfully made contact with the authorities and later that morning a rescue helicopter evacuated Wiseman and took him to the Alamosa County Hospital in the San Luis Valley. Wiseman suffered from numerous bites, a broken right leg, and hypothermia. His body temperature had dropped to 94.8 degrees Fahrenheit. After several weeks of convalescing, he was able to return to work.

On September 25, Dick Weldon, the District Wildlife Manager of the Colorado Division of Wildlife, Division employee Bob Rouse, and one of Wiseman's employees traveled to the scene in a DOW helicopter, which was slightly damaged as it landed. Weldon and the pilot were compelled to walk out to Platoro Reservoir, while Rouse and the guide stayed behind to skin the bear. What they found, much to their surprise, was a fully grown female grizzly bear. The next day a second helicopter removed the skull and hide. Unfortunately, the carcass and reproductive organs, still relatively fresh, were left at the site. Had these been saved, it could have been possible to determine whether the bear had ever borne cubs. It was not until September 29, six days after the incident, that a third helicopter was sent to repair the damaged helicopter and retrieve the bear carcass. This helicopter also crashed while leaving Platoro for Alamosa, but no one was hurt, and the carcass was eventually placed in the freezer at the La Jara Fish Hatchery.

An autopsy showed that the grizzly had died from internal hemorrhage resulting from a deep wound inflicted between the second and third ribs, severing the arch of the aorta. The fact that this fatal wound had not been described in testimony and would have been difficult to administer with a hand-held arrow of the type described by Wiseman, has resulted in some controversy about what actually occurred that night at Blue Lake. Some critics have maintained that the bear did not attack first, but had been previously wounded and was being stalked by the same party. Regardless of speculation and conjecture, the net result was one dead grizzly bear, one injured hunter, and one amazed scientific community. The greatest tragedy, perhaps, was that a prime female, fully capable of breeding, had been removed from what can best be described as a relict population.

Further study of the bear revealed, in the annual rings of a sectioned tooth, that it was more than sixteen years old, that it had weighed around three hundred pounds, and that it was in excellent physical condition. The uterus, having spoiled, could not be examined for placental scars. Division of Wildlife researcher Tom Beck, who examined the pelt, remarked to me that the bear's mammaries, in their pigmentation and size, indicated to him a good possibility that she had borne cubs before. A biologist with the Denver

Natural History Museum told me the same thing. The pelt squared at six and a half feet, and through 1985 was on temporary exhibit together with the skull and other artifacts at the Denver Natural History Museum.

I had the opportunity to examine the skull and skin of the Wiseman grizzly in the zoology department of the Denver Natural History Museum while researching this book. The pelt, in prime fall condition, is one of the most beautiful fur pelts I have ever seen. The fur is extraordinary both for its lush pelage and for its many different colors. As in the Lone Cone grizzly pelt described by Merritt Cary earlier in this chapter, the Wiseman pelt has a great variety of color patterns in it. The head ranges in color from sandy on the muzzle to dark brown around the ears. There is a distinct mantle of silver and gray on the shoulder, and here the hairs are very long. The lower legs are dark, almost charcoal, becoming a walnut brown farther up toward the body. The back is honey colored and the rump is a reddish brown.

Compared with the pelt, the skull is not in very good condition. The teeth are worn down, badly chipped, and have very little enamel (some of the tooth damage could have occurred during the boiling of the skull). The upper right canine tooth is worn to a nub. It also appears there was an abcess in its root that had rotted completely through the bone of the skull in that region. The front claws are about three inches long and extend more or less straight out, without the shorter curvature of the black bear. Two claws are missing, one on the right fore foot and the other on the left hind foot. There appear to be some arrowhead-sized holes around the throat, although this is difficult to determine because an incision was made roughly over the sternum or breastbone into the throat region. There appears to be an arrowhead-sized hole on the right leg that could have been made by the arrow that struck the heart between the second and third rib and killed the bear. This would have been a difficult wound to inflict with a hand-held arrow however, as it is round and arrows only produce such a configuration after being released from the bow (the angle of the fletching causes the arrow to spin in a circular fashion). A hand-held arrow would produce a jagged-edged wound, similar to those that appear to be present in the throat region.

The incident prompted the Colorado Division of Wildlife to launch a three-year investigation (later reduced to two years), in coordination with the affected federal land management agencies (Rio Grande and San Juan National Forest), and the owners of the Banded Peak Ranch, formerly the Tierra Amarilla Land Grant. This was done not only to fulfill immense public and scientific curiosity about whether or not the grizzly still survived in the San Juans, but also in accordance with the Endangered Species Act of 1973, which mandates both the preservation of "critical habitat" and its proper evaluation and delineation. The search was concentrated in the general vicinity of the 1979 incident: the south San Juans. The area is more than four hundred square miles in size (a quarter of a million acres), and is situated on both sides of the Continental Divide in Mineral and Archuleta counties, just north of the New Mexico border. Prominent drainages include the San Juan, Rio Blanco, Navajo, Rio Chama, and Conejos rivers. The primeval core of this region was set aside in 1980 as the 127,721-acre South San Juan Wilderness Area. Because it is so remote, it is an ideal sanctuary for the grizzly bear, an animal that requires large integrated tracts of wilderness where man's presence is essentially insignificant. It is not surprising that the last grizzlies had withdrawn into this pristine refuge, far from the roads and haunts of men.

The primary objectives of the DOW investigation were to capture and document the existence of the grizzly bear in the southern Rockies, to investigate the distribution and seasonal habitat of the grizzly bear, and to determine causes of mortality. For this purpose, the Division assembled five employees, led by wildlife researcher Tom Beck, who had for the past six years been studying black bears in a portion of Gunnison National Forest (Black Mesa). Standard field techniques, perfected over the seventies by research teams in the northern Rockies, were employed by the study group. First, and most importantly in terms of ground reconnaissance, the study season was divided into three distinct time segments: May 1 to June 30, July 1 to August 31, and September 1 to October 30. At each time, the grizzly, like the more plentiful black bear, would be feeding at different elevations and in specific microhabitats. Most of the field work was done on the ground and on foot. Little funding existed for aerial reconnaissance. Additionally, bait-trapped snare lines, some as long as six miles in length, were set at various locations on the range.

The empirical results of the two-year investigation can be summarized as follows: 1) At one remote headwater location, in an open-timbered spruce-fir stringer between two avalanche chutes, at approximately 10,665 feet, a probable denning site of a grizzly bear was found. The interior was partially collapsed. The tunnel was approximately two feet wide and two feet high. The den showed remarkable similarities to grizzly bear dens in the northern Rockies. No bedding material or hair was found. It apparently was excavated and then abandoned; 2) Approximately fifty yards west of

The skull of the female grizzly bear killed near Blue Lake in Colorado on September 23, 1979. Her teeth, particularly her upper right canine, were extremely worn and had lost much of their enamel. One scientist has postulated that this enamel loss may have been related to distemper. *Jim Halfpenny*

an alpine lake at 11,460 feet, a large feeding site for love root was found, pockmarked with many digs, and approximately a foot wide and half a foot deep. Old daybeds and root-filled scats were found in the vicinity of this site, which was located in an open-timbered sidehill park. Age of this probable grizzly bear excavation was estimated at three to five years; 3) Another dig, for biscuitroot, was found nearby on a xeric (deficient in moisture) slope at 11,653 feet. Biscuitroot has been identified as an important staple in the grizzly bear diet in the northern Rockies. Six digs of similar size to those described above were found. The age of this probable grizzly bear excavation was put at one to three years; 4) Another large dig was found about a half mile southeast of a major peak in the study area. A marmot had been dug from its den and several very large rocks were moved. The age of this probable grizzly bear excavation was put at one to three years; and 5) In August of 1981, an outfitter reported an adult grizzly (blond, with dark

Subalpine riparian habitat on the Upper Rio Grande, looking south above the confluence with Ute Creek (elevation of the river bed is 9,492 feet). Such valleys were once frequented by grizzlies in the early spring, when succulent streamside vegetation began to green up, and winter-killed deer and elk could be found. Rio Grande Pyramid (13,821 feet) is visible in the far background, fourteen miles farther up Ute Creek. A two- or three-year-old grizzly was trapped and killed on the west side of Ute Ridge in September 1951. *John Murray*

legs, weight estimated at over three hundred pounds) and two cubs in the headwaters of a major river in the study area. Personnel who visited the site found a large dig for osmorhiza. There is some speculation that it could have been the same black bear and cubs that had been sighted five miles away a few days before.

Tom Beck's final report at the end of 1982, when the program was terminated primarily because of funding shortages in the Division, made these conclusions:

1.) No further search efforts are warranted, 2.) Failure to capture a grizzly does not mean absence of grizzly bears. Management for conditions which minimize human disturbance should be continued, 3.) Livestock owners should be accordingly advised, and 4.) All bear hunters in southern Colorado should also be advised.

The previous year, in a report to the Division, he had made even more specific recommendations and observations regarding the grizzly bear and its habitat in the San Juans, including the following: 1) He observed that trail corridors, the Blue Lake area, and "The Three Forks" area, all areas of high recreational use, are areas of potential conflict with grizzly bears; 2) Areas designated as domestic sheep allotments are conflict areas; 3) The Elk Creek area provides good habitat through mid-June, but then dwindles to zero after that time because of cattle and human use. He recommended avoidance of early season use; 4) The Canon Escondido area and adjacent Canon Verde were noted as having high potential habitat value. He again recommended plans that would discourage human use of these areas; and 5) He recommended that management plans limit access to the area designated as the "Navajo River-Banded Peak-Rio Chama-Archuleta Creek" area, as it appears to be potentially good grizzly habitat and could be "the core of the existing habitat." Beck recommended that no new trails be established in this potentially sensitive region and that existing trails be allowed to deteriorate.

It should be noted that the grizzly bear inventory project conducted by Beck's team was only one of several alternatives considered by the Division in January 1980, following the grizzly incident of September 1979. A number of possible approaches to the grizzly in the southwest region of the state were discussed at this time, ranging from doing nothing (not recommended as this would contradict federal and state legislative mandates and invite lawsuits from conservationists), to introducing grizzly bears into the area to rapidly build up the population (not recommended without knowing if there are actually grizzly bears left in the area). The Division chose the middle course of action, saying that, prior to making major management commitments, it would be desirable to know if a population did in fact exist. One memorandum in the Division files from this period, from biologist David Langlois to three other Division biologists, was critical of the proposed grizzly bear inventory project:

Two outcomes seem likely from an inventory. One is that no grizzlies will be found and we will still not know whether we have a low density population. The other outcome is that a few bears will turn up, but this seems unlikely. In fact, it would probably take many years to say anything definitive about an extremely low density population of grizzlies in such a large area. Rugged terrain, inaccessible private property, and black bear interference with bait stations also compound the problem. Although a grizzly bear

inventory would be fun, make good press, and mislead the public into thinking that we are doing something about grizzlies in the state, it should be
given a very low funding priority. Furthermore, it would be professionally
irresponsible for DOW to endorse an outside agency wasting money on this
type of wild goose chase.

Mr. Langlois's memo was, it turns out, prophetic. The project did not
conclusively prove anything and, with the evidence it did find, probably
raised more questions than it answered. It is also interesting to note that
the same memorandum considers the reintroduction of bears:

> First, I think we should ask ourselves—what is our management objective
> for the grizzly bear? The strategic plan says to "not restore the grizzly bear
> or gray wolf because of their conflict with humans". . . . However, if we
> reversed ourselves, it would be relatively simple to build up a grizzly bear
> population in just a few years through transplants. If the bears stayed out of
> trouble and were not all shot we easily could restore the grizzly to a small
> portion of its former range in the state.

Recognizing the difficulties of such an endeavor, though, the author of the
memorandum concluded that "regardless of the biological feasibility, social,
economic, and political factors make a restoration program unpopular."
    Prior to this internal discussion of grizzly restoration, the subject had
been examined by the state on several earlier occasions. Part of this was
probably related to the passage of the Endangered Species Act in 1973, the
adoption of similar legislation by the state in 1973, the formation of a state
nongame management program in 1973, and, perhaps most important, the
federal listing of the grizzly as a Threatened Species in the lower forty-eight
in 1975. In 1976 nongame manager John Torres wrote a "Proposal for the
study of wolf and grizzly bear in Colorado" and a formal application for
federal funding assistance, with the project to begin on July 15, 1977. The
purpose of this project would have been, quoting from the proposal:

> "To determine potential for reintroduction of Wolf and Grizzly Bear in Colo-
> rado and implement said introduction. Ultimately the Wolf and Grizzly Bear
> would be removed from the endangered list."

The proposal outlines in detail the step-by-step process for a wolf and grizzly
reintroduction in Colorado. This proposal was never funded or implemented
by the Division and, in 1977, the Division formally stated its opposition

to wolf or grizzly reintroduction "because of their conflict with humans."

In the same year the Forbes Trinchera Ranch, a 262-square-mile private ranch near Ft. Garland in the San Luis Valley, was offered to the state of Colorado as "a release site for the introduction of grizzly bear in Colorado" by Mr. Forbes, the owner. Adjacent ranches—the 77,000 acre Taylor Ranch and the 90,000 acre Blanco Trinchera Ranch—raised no objections to a grizzly restoration. Walt Barber, the manager of the Taylor Ranch, said "he would provide reasonable protection for the bear if it came onto the Taylor Ranch." The wildlife manager for the Blanco Trinchera, Mr. Denton (a former DOW wildlife conservation officer), stated that he believed "that CO_2 guns presently used to protect sheep from black bear, would keep the grizzly away from the sheep." This grizzly reintroduction plan was formally submitted to the Colorado Wildlife Commission for consideration. The Commission rejected the proposal. Disadvantages of a grizzly release on private land mentioned at the time include the fact that the public would never have an opportunity to see the grizzlies, a huntable population would never be achieved, and the bears might wander off the ranch and kill livestock or worse in surrounding areas, with negative legal ramifications. On the surface it seemed an excellent opportunity to restore the grizzly to a secure location in Colorado, but it was doomed by the political exigencies of the time. Also during this period John Craighead submitted a grizzly reintroduction plan to the state of Colorado for the San Juan Mountains. This proposal was also rejected.

At the present time, the existence of the grizzly bear in Colorado remains an open question. In the best possible case, it is thought a small relict population exists, and that it is endangered both through man-induced mortality (including unreported incidents involving sheep or cattle) and the effects of inbreeding. Some biologists, like Tom Beck, doubt whether inbreeding is a problem for grizzlies, and point to small isolated populations in Europe, such as those in the Apennine Mountains of Italy or the Pyrenees Mountains of the French/Spanish border, that have persisted for over one hundred years, as evidence the grizzly is not as susceptible to inbreeding as are other mammals. Others, like Chris Servheen, U.S. Fish and Wildlife Grizzly Bear Recovery Coordinator, disagree, and believe that isolated populations will eventually self-destruct because of inbreeding and its genetic consequences. In the worst possible case it is thought that the Wiseman grizzly in 1979 was the last grizzly in Colorado, or that the remaining individuals cannot breed because they are too widely dispersed, they are of the same sex, or they are simply too old to reproduce. There may also be only one grizzly left. Because of the unknown status of the grizzly at this time, there is no management plan, either passive or active, and none contemplated. In January 1982, the Colorado Wildlife Commission went on record with a resolution opposing the restoration of either the grizzly or the wolf in Colorado. The 1982 *Grizzly Bear Recovery Plan* for the lower forty-eight states, while making note of the Wiseman incident in 1979 and the follow-up study, only briefly mentions the grizzly in Colorado:

> The remoteness of the area [south San Juans], its proximity to wilderness areas and the existence of a very large and well protected Spanish Land Grant, Tierra Amarilla [The Banded Peak Ranch], all lend credibility to the possible existence of a relict population. This plan does not address recovery in Colorado beyond expressing hope that a search for grizzlies will continue.

Elsewhere, the recovery plan reports that, "the status of the grizzly bear in the San Juan National Forest in Colorado is still in doubt."

Where do we go from here? There are essentially two courses of action with the grizzly in Colorado. One is to assume that there are no grizzlies in the state and give them no recognition in wildlife planning, or to assume that a small population possibly exists, but still give it no protection. This is the status quo, and further assumes that given present realities in the state, it is doubtful that a reintroduction could now take place. The other course of action is to assume that there are grizzlies in the state and give them some formal status in planning and management, such as curtailing bear hunting in some areas south of Wolf Creek Pass and north of Cumbres Pass (Big Game Units 78 and 81), advising big-game hunters entering the area that there may be grizzlies and that they are protected, and similarly advising stockmen using grazing allotments on federal land in the area that grizzlies may be around and should not be disturbed.

This second course of action also raises a more controversial question: Should the grizzly be restored to the area of the San Juan Mountains, or perhaps some other area deemed suitable for it (and for man)?

If it were to be considered, The Endangered Species Act of 1973, as amended in 1982, does contain provisions for such an action. New populations of endangered or threatened species are known as "experimental populations" and may be created "outside the current range of such species if the Secretary (of the Interior) determines that such release will further the conservation of such species." The reintroduction of the gray wolf into Yellowstone National Park, a project currently proposed in the Northern

Rocky Mountain Timber Wolf Recovery Plan, would be considered an "experimental population." If the grizzly were restored in Colorado under these provisions, it would be considered, like the wolf in Yellowstone, a nonessential experimental population; that is, an experimental release of animals to help the preservation of the species as a whole, but not essential to its survival on Earth.

Has anyone seriously made such a proposal for Colorado in recent years? The answer is yes, but not in official quarters. Support for such an effort has come from a variety of other sources. Bill Schneider, for example, formerly the editor of *Montana Outdoors* (the bimonthly magazine of the Montana Game and Fish Department), proposed a number of new grizzly sanctuaries in his popular book *Where The Grizzly Walks*, including the River of No Return Wilderness (now the Frank Church Wilderness) in Idaho, the Anaconda-Pintlar Wilderness in Montana, the Bridger Wilderness in Wyoming, Rocky Mountain National Park in Colorado, the Flattops Wilderness Area in Colorado, the Weminuche Wilderness in Colorado, the Gila Wilderness and the Aldo Leopold Wilderness in New Mexico, and the Blue Range Primitive Area in Arizona and New Mexico. David Brown, Game Branch Supervisor for the Arizona Game and Fish Department and author of several books on endangered species in the Southwest, including *The Grizzly in the Southwest, Documentary of an Extinction*, has recommended the grizzly be returned to the areas Schneider suggests for southern Arizona and southern New Mexico. In a recent issue of *Bear News*, the quarterly publication of the Great Bear Foundation based in Missoula, Montana, Brown discussed grizzly restoration in Colorado's San Juans as well. He stated: "A Southwesterner shouldn't have to go to Yellowstone or Glacier to see a silvertip. Not with all the wilderness we have in bear country."

Many people feel that although a Colorado restoration plan has its merits, the government should, because of limited funding and personnel, concentrate on those areas where the grizzly has the best chance. As Paul Schullery wrote in his book *The Bears of Yellowstone*:

> The most optimistic defenders of the bear would like to reestablish grizzly populations in some parts of its former range in the Rockies. That is an intriguing idea, but first we must concentrate on guaranteeing the survival of existing populations, like the bears of Yellowstone.

Others feel that, because of the seriousness of a situation in which the grizzly may become extinct even in Yellowstone, aggressive action should be taken immediately, wherever it is feasible. As Tom McNamee wrote in his recent book *The Grizzly Bear*:

> One of the strongest criticisms of the grizzly bear recovery plan has been that it identifies only . . . six areas for grizzly restoration. Quite a few conservationists feel that many more pieces of ancestral grizzly range could support viable populations with only minimal management expense. In other words, if you released a sufficient number of wild grizzlies there, left them alone and tried to keep people from killing them, they might well thrive. And if they didn't, it is argued, so what? There are plenty of wild grizzlies available for relocation from Canada and Alaska, so you could still try again, or even decide it was a bad idea and forget it.

Colorado wildlife researcher Tom Beck speaks for many, and summarizes the situation well, in a note he made while reading this book in manuscript form:

> [There is] no question that the physical habitat for grizzly bears exists in Colorado. That really isn't an issue. What is an issue is 1986 mankind's intolerance for grizzly bears in Colorado. Change the attitudes first before sacrificing the bears [in a recovery effort]. My feelings are I have never known of a grizzly bear I disliked enough to turn loose in Colorado.

Beck's views are similar to many I encountered, in government and out of government, from conservationists whose concern is chiefly for the bear—if people's attitudes could be changed (no small chore), then it might be possible. But, they say, that is a big if. Similarly, John Craighead has written in his book *A Definitive System for Analysis of Grizzly Bear Habitat and Other Wilderness Resources*:

> Transplanting grizzly bears from one region to another to augment an existing population or to reestablish a historical one has intrigued wildlife managers. The requisite technology is available; the legal, social, political, economic and philosophical requirements are not. It is unlikely that any substantial progress will be made in resolving these issues until a specific reestablishment project is authorized for agency and public consideration.

Both Beck and Craighead, as biologists, are pragmatists and realize that the issue is politically and socially complex and involves many groups: livestock interests, local residents, politicians, environmentalists, logging interests, mining interests, skiing interests, and state and federal land management

Subalpine meadowland on Weminuche Pass looking south, deep in the Weminuche Wilderness Area. This is classic summer range for grizzlies, with a diversity of important feeding areas nearby. Although grizzlies today would probably avoid such low cover areas as Weminuche Pass, they were observed in this general vicinity throughout the 1960s and 1970s. The last report occurred in the summer of 1976, when a bear believed to be a grizzly was sighted near Hossack Lake about eight miles to the southeast. It is still possible that grizzlies inhabit these remote high mountain areas along the Continental Divide. *John Murray*

and wildlife agencies. The contemplation of a grizzly reintroduction touches all of these and more.

Opponents and proponents of a grizzly reintroduction in Colorado make equally convincing arguments for their respective positions. Opponents of such a project have the stronger hand at this point in time, primarily because the Division of Wildlife has opposed grizzly reintroduction in their Strategic Plan, and the Wildlife Commission, appointed by the governor to oversee the agency, has passed a formal resolution also opposing grizzly reintroduction. Any effort to restore the grizzly in the state would have to convince these two groups of the wisdom, efficacy, and suitability of the project, and that would not be easy. Some would say it would be impossible (at least at the present time). The position of the Division and the Commission merits closer examination.

The first concern of state officials with respect to the grizzly is public safety. The bear is a large and potentially dangerous animal. Incidents could occur, either on public or private land, in which a person might be mauled or even killed. It is possible that the doctrine of sovereign immunity, which ordinarily protects the state from lawsuit, could not be raised as a defense in a claim arising from a grizzly attack. There is the potential for a lawsuit here, and a potentially large settlement could arise from it. We live in a litigious society, and there is also a legitimate concern for public safety.

A second concern of the state is that of damages arising from grizzly bear livestock depredations. The state already pays out in excess of $750,000 per year for damage done to livestock by black bears and lions, and to crops by antelope, mule deer, and elk. The agency would naturally prefer not to get involved with any more of these time-consuming and expensive damage settlements.

Another economic concern of the state is how its money is spent. Those entrusted with making the decisions about how best to allocate finite resources try to measure expenditures by how well they benefit the most people—how is the common good best served? These officials, people like Jim Ruch, the Director of the Division of Wildlife, and Tim Schultz, the Chairman of the Colorado Wildlife Commission, would question the value of giving the grizzly bear an annual chunk of the budget—might the money be better spent in purchasing prairie chicken habitat, or in the river otter recovery, or in helping the greenback trout? If the grizzly bear was only found in Colorado and was endangered here, they would feel compelled to help it—but the fact is, it isn't. There are other areas where it is doing fine, like Canada and Alaska. Those areas, it is argued, are the best places for the grizzly in the modern world.

Other arguments often raised against grizzly reintroduction include that the project would be management-intensive and would require too much effort for too little return, that there is insufficient habitat (including the critical spring-range component), that the recovery would have major negative impact on multiple use of the public lands, that there are not enough grizzlies elsewhere to successfully build up a new population, that we do not yet know how to move grizzlies successfully from one place to the next, and that, in short, we simply do not have the societal acceptance of the grizzly necessary to make the sacrifices which would be needed to restore it and to coexist with it. Among opponents there is the sense that it would be impossible to form a working alliance among the diverse interests that would be impacted by a grizzly restoration, a partnership necessary to insure its acceptance in a pluralistic society. In particular, there is the belief that livestock interests could never be convinced to go along with it because their livelihoods would be threatened.

Equally interesting arguments can be made in favor of grizzly bear restoration. First, with regard to the legal situation, it is to be acknowledged that an incident involving a human and a bear could, and probably would, occur at some point in time. However, the unsuitability of the doctrine of sovereign immunity as a defense could be questioned. If the state took proper precautions in informing the public they were entering a grizzly sanctuary, they could adequately defend themselves in court if a person were hurt by a grizzly. This could be done with signs at trailheads, warnings as to how to behave in grizzly country, and other precautionary practices standard in Wyoming, Montana, and Alaska, where people often enter the domain of the grizzly.

Although it is true that under certain circumstances grizzly bears are dangerous, much of what has been written about the species has been wildly exaggerated. As Chris Servheen wrote in a recent scientific paper:

> There is some evidence that [grizzly] bears which live in highly disturbed areas are able to either learn how to avoid activity areas, habituate to activities, or to vary their diel periods of activity and use of cover to successfully exploit resources in disturbed areas with little conflict with man.

Tom Beck, writing his initial Environmental Assessment for the South San Juan Grizzly Bear Survey in 1980, made a similar observation of the reclusiveness of these animals: ". . . bears in this area have long been persecuted by man and may have responded by adopting extreme aversion behavior." That the Wiseman grizzly killed in 1979 had successfully avoided being seen or detected for over sixteen years in an intensely used backcountry area is a tribute to the intelligence of the species and its willingness to adapt to humans, if given the opportunity. To those who would unfairly play upon public fears and apprehensions, it is evidence that the bear can exist peacefully with humans, as it has, and still does, in many other parts of the Rockies.

The facts attest to the compatibility of the grizzly with humans. Since 1900 only fifteen people have been killed by grizzly bears in the lower forty-eight states. As a matter of statistical record, stinging insects have accounted for more deaths in America during this time period than grizzly bears. Also in the same period, over 2.5 million people have died in automobile accidents, with fifty thousand more killed each year. Hundreds die each year in airplane crashes. The chances of drowning in grizzly country, or even of being struck by lightning, are actually greater than the chances of a grizzly attack. Additionally, it has been shown that most of those fifteen incidents involved "garbage" bears, animals habituated to people through feeding on human foods.

Grizzlies released in Colorado would be truly wild bears, selected for their history of nonconflict with man, and would be kept this way by managers. Further, a vigorous program of public education, coupled with the use of secure food storage facilities in backcountry areas, and other practices, could help prevent unnecessary confrontations. People would then have to weigh the value of entering an ecosystem in which they are not the dominant species against the remote chance of an incident. If they felt uncomfortable in the area in which grizzlies were found, probably only a fraction of the wilderness of Colorado, they could simply go elsewhere in the state.

The grizzly does not present the conflict with livestock that its reputation would seem to indicate. Chris Servheen reported to me that, in 1985, only thirty sheep were killed by grizzly bears in all six population areas in the lower forty-eight states. The overall grizzly population south of Canada he estimates to range between six hundred and nine hundred animals. With regard to cattle, he wrote to me in the same letter that "in my experience, only a handful of cattle are killed in the lower forty-eight states on the average by grizzly bears and in most years, none at all." Because of isolated depredations, the grizzly has been subjected throughout the Rockies to excessive predator control measures. The fact is, most grizzlies do not cause livestock depredations. The bears have the greatest intestinal length relative to body length of any carnivore, which helps them to digest their largely vegetative diet of roots, berries, bulbs, leaves, and nuts. Many studies on the food habits of the bear in the lower forty-eight have shown that they eat meat only seasonally: carrion in the spring, rodents and fish in the summer, rut-weakened ungulates prior to denning.

How could the livestock interests' needs be addressed with regard to grizzly depredations? In both Norway and Italy brown bear managers offer woolgrowers twice the market rate for documented bear kills. This prevents marginal operations from going under because of depredations, and offers livestock interests a positive incentive not to eliminate the bears. If an individual bear were to become a problem, managers could deal with it accordingly under a zone management system as is currently used for nuisance bears in the six grizzly ecosystems in the lower forty-eight states.

A central core area offers more or less complete protection – this would be the heart of the official grizzly bear refuge. Roughly concentric management areas around the inner area would allow greater flexibility, including removing a chronic problem animal from the population. Further use of technology could also help with managing the bears compatibly with livestock grazing, including radio-mapping the bears, manipulating time of entry or use of certain areas or allotments, and, possibly, the use of anesthetic collars to safely immobilize nuisance bears.

In August 1986 I spoke with Art Dimeo, the Assistant District Ranger for the Conejos District of the Rio Grande National Forest (most of the South San Juan Wilderness Area east of the Continental Divide) about livestock grazing in his part of the San Juans. Surprisingly enough, livestock grazing has greatly declined in this area, and is not expected to approach its former levels. Mr. Dimeo reported to me that many allotments are either completely vacant or only partially stocked. The reasons, he believes, are threefold. First, economics has negatively impacted the livestock industry. Meat prices currently make it unprofitable to work with sheep and cattle, and foreign wool competition has hurt domestic wool production. Second, there is a generational factor. Young people in the area aren't interested in pursuing what they believe is a marginal livelihood. Third, there is the climate of the San Juans. The mountains are known for their heavy precipitation, which can mean hoof rot in the summer (for both sheep and cattle) and devastating blizzards both early and late in the season. The livestock industry will always be using these mountains, but it is clear they will never be the dominant force on these public lands they once were. After speaking with representatives from the woolgrowers and cattlemen in Colorado, I believe the industry might one day be convinced to go along with a grizzly restoration. Of paramount importance would be the protection of their livelihoods. If the continued multiple use of the public lands could be assured, it is possible an agreement could be reached.

It would admittedly be difficult to justify a large expenditure for grizzly restoration in an era of fiscal conservatism, but that justification does depend on one's value system and how one prioritizes endangered species. With regard to the issue of game-damage claims, it is possible grizzly claims would be in the range of acceptability, given the figures Servheen reports for Montana and Wyoming. It is also possible that conservation organizations ranging from the Audubon Society to the United Sportsmen's Council could be convinced to donate to a fund for game damage, as well as provide rewards for illegal grizzly kills.

Some biologists, such as Dr. Tony Povilitis of the University of Colo-

Alpine tundra at the headwaters of Ute Creek along the Continental Divide in the Weminuche Wilderness Area. The view is north, looking toward Twin Lakes and Rio Grande Pyramid. Lloyd Anderson, a government trapper who killed one of the last grizzlies in 1952, observed a sow and two cubs feeding at this approximate location in the summer of 1967. It is possible that the bears were feeding on the roots of the alpine bistort, visible here as an extensive carpet of small white flowers in the foreground. *John Murray*

rado, have hypothesized that man has exerted, and is continuing to exert, a significant evolutionary pressure on the grizzly south of Canada, a selective force that has steadily removed many of the more aggressive, widely roaming bears from the breeding populations. This has had the effect, they believe, of working to produce a "different" sort of grizzly, a bear becoming similar in some respects to the European brown bear, which has evolved side by side with man for several thousand years in densely populated Europe. Brown bears tend to be both smaller and less aggressive than their Holarctic relatives in North America. While it is true the situation is lamentable in terms of the original integrity of the grizzly line, it is possible that this is the only way in which man and the grizzly can coexist in areas of high human population, and that the respective species are reaching a "compromise" with nature and evolution. Grizzlies brought into Colorado would have emerged from the same process, and would continue to be subject to the same pressure, possibly leading to a bear more adapted to people and livestock in the Colorado of the twenty-first century.

Most biologists with whom I spoke in the course of researching this book believe that we have the habitat for the grizzly in Colorado (while also agreeing that we do not yet have the social acceptability for the species). A natural question facing people interested in grizzly bear recovery would be: Where would you put the bears? And, as a caveat, although we have many fragmented portions of the species' former range, do we now have any one area large enough to support a viable population in perpetuity? The first place that comes to mind is the last place where the grizzly has been found in Colorado: the San Juans. The Weminuche Wilderness Area and the South San Juan Wilderness Area together offer well over nine hundred square miles of designated wilderness area, an area known to be good black bear habitat as well as to have historically (as well as possibly presently) supported grizzly bears. Also, the wilderness area part of the San Juans is surrounded by over one thousand square miles of National Forest land at lower elevations. Both spring range and summer range are found in this area. From Spring Creek Pass south along the Continental Divide to Cumbres Pass on the New Mexico border, the San Juans offer an enormous integrated section of mountain wilderness, crossed by only one paved road— U.S. 160 at Wolf Creek Pass—in over 150 miles. That the mountain complex has been retained in much of its original wildness is indeed fortuitous. While it is true that many parts of the forest and the wilderness are intensely used by backcountry enthusiasts, it is also probably true that management techniques and guidelines could be developed to allow the bears and people to exist as compatibly as they can.

Not all people think that the San Juans are the only, or possibly even the best, place for a grizzly reintroduction. With respect to the San Juans, Tom Beck writes: "I have studied Colorado bears for eight years and I think there are better places and some just as good—but surely not only one totally unique place." Other areas that had grizzly bears in the twentieth century that Beck feels would have to be looked at include the West Elk Wilderness Area, the Uncompahgre Plateau, Grand Mesa, and the Wilson Mountains. While some people might also suggest Rocky Mountain National Park as a possible location (approximately four hundred square miles in the north-central mountains of the state) it probably would not hold up under scrutiny. With about 2.2 million visitors per year (as much as Yellowstone) the same Park in which nature writer and park founder Enos Mills once tracked a grizzly for two days is probably too crowded to now support the grizzly.

It would be premature to discuss in detail techniques that might be used for restoring grizzlies in Colorado—much of it is only theory at this point anyway—but there are several bright areas of research that might one day be relevant. First, it seems likely that bears with no history of conflict with mankind or livestock would be logical candidates. Sows would be preferred over boars in general because they are usually homebodies—using smaller home ranges—and because they have more potential to add to the population. Unacceptable would be problem bears—bears that other states are trying to get rid of because of a history of difficulties with them (an offer by Montana to give us some of their nuisance bears was politely and wisely turned down by the Division in 1985).

Second, it is possible that grizzly bear cubs can be interspecifically cross-fostered to black bear sows. Chris Servheen is currently researching this technique in the Cabinet Mountains of Montana. In this approach, "grizzly cubs specially bred in zoological parks are placed in the natal den of a pre-selected black bear sow who has recently borne cubs." This transfer takes place in the early spring. Intraspecific cross-fostering has been demonstrated with black bears in cases where orphaned cubs were placed with adult females who had cubs of the same age. In the majority of cases, the black bear cubs were adopted by the new mother. Some biologists believe that grizzly cubs raised by a black bear sow might differ behaviorally. The relationship between mother and cub is all important in bear society. It is possible a grizzly raised by a black bear sow known to be reclusive might be safer in habitat that has more people in it. If research proves this technique reliable, it could become a valuable management tool in areas in which existing grizzly bear populations are being augmented, or in which historic range is being re-colonized.

Third, computerized satellite-mapping techniques could be used to evaluate potential grizzly bear habitat in Colorado, thus helping to answer many questions about the feasibility of such a project. John Craighead has written of this possibility in his book *A Definitive System for Analysis of Grizzly Bear Habitat and Other Wilderness Resources*:

> Restoring grizzly bear populations by transplant has been considered for the Selway-Bitterroot Wilderness of Idaho and for the San Juan Wilderness of Colorado. Should public and agency interest in such projects become serious, the first procedural step would be to map and describe the ecosystem using multispectral imagery and computer technology. This would provide a quantitative basis for evaluating the habitat and for comparing it directly with ecosystems similarly mapped, but supporting viable grizzly bear popu-

lations. The size of a self-sustaining population varies with the intrinsic dynamics of the species and with the quality and quantity of habitat. The higher the quality of habitat, the fewer animal transplants should be required for a viable re-establishment. The definitive resource analysis system described would enable planners to find specific answers to such questions and to obtain a broad view of the biological problems involved before any commitment is made.

Any such evaluation based on vegetative mapping in the San Juans would also have to look closely at human use and how it would be affected by the presence of grizzly bears. New computer technology now permits forest managers in the northern Rockies to fairly precisely determine the impact of the two species upon one another in a given area at a given time of the year. The same techniques could help elsewhere.

It must be stressed, in looking at grizzly restoration, that scientists currently do not know how to transfer large numbers of grizzlies from one area to another. It has, quite simply, never been done before. It is known that black bears can be successfully reintroduced in large numbers. Arkansas restocked 254 black bears from 1959 through 1967. Louisiana restocked 161 black bears from 1964 through 1967. This gives biologists reason to believe grizzlies probably can be successfully reintroduced, but the exact means remains an unanswered question.

How many grizzly bears would it take? Computer modeling studies for grizzly bear habitat in the northern Rockies have suggested that for a minimum area of 965 square miles it is necessary to have between 70 and 90 bears on a sustained basis for a minimum viable population. An MVP, as it is known, is defined as "the smallest population having a ninety-five per cent chance of surviving one hundred years." Several biologists with whom I spoke while researching this book believe that these Montana habitats are sufficiently analogous, in terms of food productivity, cover availability, and denning locations, to habitats found in the San Juans so that data from these studies could be relevant to southwestern Colorado. The Division of Wildlife's 1980 Environmental Assessment, prepared by biologist Tom Beck, stated in its discussion of restoration as a management option (while not endorsing it as policy), that "An introduction should be 40–60 bears in size." A higher figure would probably be more realistic, particularly when it is considered that, at least initially, mortality would probably exceed natality, and that more, rather than fewer, bears would be required to insure the protection of the population.

Another factor to be considered is that of the genetics of isolated mammal populations. A recent workshop on the genetics of grizzly bear populations at the International Grizzly Bear Conference (1986) focused on the need to simulate natural gene flow in isolated populations (such as are found in Yellowstone National Park and in the Cabinet Mountains of Montana). Scientists concluded that it will be necessary to periodically introduce new bears into these areas. As biologist Chris Servheen stated in a paper on the subject:

> The rate of gene flow recommended as necessary to maintain genetic viability was at least one successfully breeding individual per generation. For grizzly bears, mean generation time was estimated at eight years. . . artificial maintenance of gene flow levels must be managed through augmentation.

The same would be true for any populations established in Colorado, or elsewhere in the Southwest.

The issue of grizzly restoration in the San Juan Mountains will be further complicated by on-going developments in the 1980s and 1990s, such as the construction of summer homes on potential spring range, the use or activation of mining claims deep in the wilderness, the building of logging roads on national forest land, increasing recreational use of the backcountry, the possible creation of new dams and water diversion projects, continued low-level grazing, and, perhaps most ominously in the immediate future, the construction of new ski resorts and associated housing projects. In December 1986, for example, the U.S. Forest Service announced that it had formally approved Wolf Creek Valley, a new ski resort and housing development on the west side of Wolf Creek Pass that will accommodate ten thousand skiers a day and will support three thousand houses and apartments. Residents, wildlife biologists, and environmentalists have so far prevented the development of the back bowls, an area between the East Fork and West Fork of the San Juan River close to both the South San Juan Wilderness Area and the Weminuche Wilderness Area. This area is critically important to both deer and elk. If grizzlies were to be restored to the San Juans, the back bowl region would comprise an important bear travel corridor between the southern San Juans and the middle and northern San Juans (along the Divide to Spring Creek Pass). Such developments will make it more difficult to protect the San Juan ecosystem in the years to come, and will complicate efforts to restore endangered animals such as the grizzly. Construction is scheduled to begin on the new Wolf Creek Valley resort in June 1992. The back bowls—an area of about 640 acres—would be only a small portion of the projected 4,290 acre ski area (1,726 acres of which would be on the San Juan National Forest).

As a means of providing at least one sizeable location in a San Juan Grizzly Bear Sanctuary or Refuge in which the bears would be completely protected, one possibility is that much of the appropriate federally-owned land south of Wolf Creek Pass, currently the South San Juan Wilderness Area and its environs, could be redesignated the South San Juan National Park. Not only would the medium-sized (250,000 acres) park be an economic asset to three or four of the poorest counties in Colorado (in Conejos County unemployment has recently exceeded eighteen per cent, with nearly fifty per cent of the adult population on welfare), but it would also help to funnel off some of the visitors to Rocky Mountain National Park, which, though one-sixth the size of Yellowstone, has the same number of visitors (over two million) annually. Grizzlies in the park, unlike those in the Weminuche Wilderness to the north, would be protected from two areas of historic conflict: grazing and hunting. Big game hunters could be provided for by the institution of post-season hunts at lower elevations, on both public and private land after the deer and elk have migrated from the park.

These would be the advantages of the park to grizzly restoration. The disadvantages are important to note. As U.S. Fish and Wildlife Grizzly Bear Recovery Coordinator Chris Servheen pointed out in comments he made on the book while it was in manuscript form:

> National Parks are not necessarily good grizzly habitat. Parks are mandated to preserve the environment "for the enjoyment of the people"—often a direct conflict with natural resource management.

Paul Schullery, formerly Park Historian at Yellowstone National Park and author of several bear books, agrees with Servheen, and feels a large sanctuary would ultimately serve the cause of the grizzly best. He believes the possibilities for a public-private cooperative sanctuary offer a rare and exciting conservation challenge, in terms of management and research, and cites as an example Great Britain, where the conservancy movement was born amid the need for preservation thwarted by the paucity of public land. Dave Brown, a wildlife biologist with the Arizona Game and Fish Department and author of *The Grizzly in the Southwest*, believes the Park concept would alienate an important wilderness constituency, the big game hunters, and that the Park Service might not be the best agency to manage the bears and their new home, anyway. He believes the Forest Service is, despite its multiple-use philosophy and orientation, fully capable of handling the project. He also believes it is dangerous to link the return of the grizzly to the establishment of a new National Park. There are too many "ifs" involved. It would be better, to his way of thinking, if proponents simply worked on grizzly recovery first and foremost. He, like Schullery, feels a sanctuary on existing land would be sufficient.

Of prime consideration to the recovery effort, whether it involved a park or not, would be the acquisition of the 77,000-acre Banded Peak Ranch, formerly the Tierra Amarilla Land Grant, either through conservation easement managed through the Nature Conservancy, Audubon Society, or other private group, or through outright purchase. In fact, federal funds exist for such a purpose, in the form of the Land and Water Conservation Fund, which is designated for land acquisition and conservation purposes, and generates around $900 million a year from offshore oil drilling leases and royalties, fees private companies pay to extract valuable minerals from the public domain. Both the East Fork of the Navajo River and the Main Fork of the Navajo River, located on the Banded Peak Ranch, constitute prime bear habitat and would be important spring and summer range for grizzlies if they were restored. Although the ranch presently has conservation-minded owners and is managed largely as a wildlife refuge, it could one day pass on to other owners who do not share this philosophy. Bringing these pristine wilderness lands into public ownership would permanently insure their protection for the American people.

Any group seriously interested in restoring the grizzly in Colorado will face an uphill battle. This is not to say that it can't be done, or shouldn't be attempted. But friends of the bear should understand that, if they try, it will be a difficult and often frustrating endeavor. While it is true that we still have the habitat and are developing the methodology, the social and political prerequisites are not yet there. Biologist Tom Beck, who probably knows more about bears than anyone in Colorado, suggests that such kindred spirits should concentrate more on how to forge the coalition of interests needed to bring back grizzly bears.

For the time being, the focus in such an effort would need to be on preliminaries. Public education comes to mind immediately, getting educational materials into the schools to dispel some of the misconceptions about grizzlies in the general population. A good, factually-based film would also help, as has been found in making a case for gray wolf restoration in Yel-

Clean hunting camps would have to be an essential part of any grizzly bear sanctuary in order to minimize bear-human contact. Game poles, such as this one in the author's 1977 hunting camp, would have to be hung higher and at a greater distance from camp. *John Murray*

lowstone National Park and its environs. Meetings with livestock representatives would be important. Only if all the diverse interests affected by the issue could be brought together under one large tent could the Wildlife Commission be expected to seriously reexamine their historic opposition to grizzly restoration. Their approval would be absolutely necessary for the discussion to move from the tabletops to the treetops.

In order to facilitate this forward movement, it will probably be necessary for a Colorado Grizzly Bear Society to be formed, similar to the Arizona Bear Society that was formed in December 1986 in Phoenix, Arizona by proponents of grizzly restoration in that state. This newly-formed, non-profit group is seriously looking into the possibility of reintroducing the grizzly bear into at least two locations in Arizona: the Blue Range Primitive Area and the adjacent San Carlos Indian Reservation (the group has an additional interest in the Gila Wilderness Area and the Aldo Leopold Wilderness Area across the border in New Mexico). In a recent article in the *Phoenix Gazette*, ABS founder and President Bill Smaltz, Senior, said, "Grizzly reintroduc-

The grizzly bear statue at the Denver Museum of Natural History. *Susan Goldstein*

tions would be a major step toward restoring our state's wildlife. . . ." Smaltz stated that his group is also interested in improving habitat for the state's black bears. Another member, Dave Brown, who is the Game Branch Supervisor for the Arizona Game and Fish Department, was quoted in the same article as saying:

> The first thing would be to gather a number of potential release sites. This would involve field trips to assure that each site would have the proper things grizzlies need, such as a cool climate, available water, canyons, grass, berry-producing shrubs, proper denning sites and other available food sources. Once you've gotten the habitat requirements documented and prime sites designated, then you would have to get the support of local ranchers and residents.

The group is attempting to locate at least one initial site where a small number of grizzlies can be released experimentally, in order to perfect the restoration techniques that will be required for a larger release program. A similar type of group could help with grizzly restoration in Colorado, as well as in New Mexico and perhaps even in California if further interest develops in those states.

Writing in 1948, the conservationist Aldo Leopold could already see what was happening to the grizzly bear in the West:

> In 1909, when I first saw the West, there were grizzlies in every major mountain mass. . . . [today] Only five states have any at all. . . . Relegating grizzlies to Alaska is about like relegating happiness to heaven; one may never get there. Saving the grizzly requires a series of large areas from which roads and livestock are excluded, or in which livestock damage is compensated.

He was indeed prophetic. The only way that the grizzly will be saved from the rising flood of humanity is by creating large areas in which the bears may roam far from man and from each other. Will there be danger of incidents in these areas? Yes. Again, though, Leopold says it best: "It must be poor life that achieves freedom from fear." Is there, realistically, any widespread public support for such conservation measures? I believe so. In November 1986, for example, I was a guest for an hour on a popular radio talk show in Denver. After an initial presentation, my host and I took live telephone calls. Every call during the time I was on the program supported the restoration of the grizzly bear in Colorado. Perhaps there is more grassroots support for the preservation of endangered predators than is commonly believed, a public longing that will need to be tapped and channeled if restoration is to succeed.

Dave Brown, in writing of the future of the grizzly in Arizona and New Mexico in his book *The Grizzly in the Southwest*, makes a statement that is as applicable to the future of the grizzly in Colorado:

> If there is a future for southwestern grizzlies, it relies not on some new-found relict population but on a planned introduction of bears experienced with man and his ways. . . . Time and proper planning are the keys—two ingredients not often present when wildlife-management decisions are made. It would be a fatal mistake to sell the public on the wrong bears too soon. It would also be too easy to procrastinate in perpetuity. Bureaucracies have demonstrated that they are prone to make both kinds of errors. . . . The time for the grizzly to reclaim his domain may yet return. If it comes, I hope it is done right. The opportunity, for success or failure, will probably only come once.

In Colorado, as in Arizona and New Mexico, supporters will have to find the ideal middle ground between equivocation and impetuosity, and proceed steadily but carefully toward their objectives. ". . . If education really educates," Aldo Leopold once wrote,

> there will, in time, be more and more citizens who understand that relics of the old West add meaning and value to the new. Youth yet unborn will pole up the Missouri with Lewis and Clark, or climb the Sierras with James Capen Adams, and each generation in turn will ask: Where is the big white bear? It will be a sorry answer to say he went under while conservationists weren't looking.

Outside the west entrance of the Denver Museum of Natural History is a large bronze sculpture of a mother grizzly and her two spring cubs. At the base of the sculpture is this inscription: "When the grizzly is gone we shall have lost the sublime specimen of wildlife that exalts the western wilderness." It is something to think about.

VIII

WINTER RANGE

THE GRAY WOLF

... the pack joined the first three hounds and could be heard in full cry, with that peculiar decoy-howl that indicates they are running a wolf ... the Count and Semyon galloped out of the thicket and on their left saw the wolf ... Semyon ... galloped off along the edge of the bushes to cut the wolf off from the cover ... But the wolf got into the bushes, and not a single hunter managed to intercept it.
—Leo Tolstoy, *War and Peace*

INTRODUCTION

The wolf has an association with humankind more ancient than civilization itself, a relationship that stretches back across the hills and valleys of time to a remote plain and an archaic period when *Homo sapiens*, like *Canis lupus*, was a nomadic and opportunistic hunter, wandering about the world in small family groups continuously in search of the necessities of life. This singular relationship, of being similar predators sharing a common history characterized by competition and conflict, has fascinated and mystified man for ages, simultaneously attracting him to, and repulsing him from, the wolf. It is a preoccupation reflected in a myriad of literary, religious, and historical references, ranging from those found in the most ancient works to those of the Middle Ages to the most contemporary sources. The wolf is, demonstrably, far more than just another animal. Mention the word "wolf" and you instantly evoke an image, command an opinion, and produce a response. The wolf as symbol resonates with a number of associations relating to humankind's lost tribal and ritualistic past, as well as to the integration with nature our species forfeited when we became civilized away from intimate involvement with natural processes. Above all, the wolf holds a disturbing mirror up to our own atavism, our tribalism and aggression and intolerance, revealing aspects of our nature that we would rather project upon an animal we can persecute and destroy than accept within ourselves.

Almost all literary, religious, and historical references to the wolf, except those found among the North American Indians, are pejorative in the extreme. This bias against the wolf, however, goes even deeper than literature. It is inextricably intertwined in the very roots of language, both in the definition of the word and in its etymology. The standard definition of the word wolf, for example, includes the following: a "fierce, rapacious, or destructive person," a "crafty person," a "man forward, direct, and zealous in amatory attentions to women," a "corrupting or destructive agency," one who "cloaks a hostile intention with a friendly manner," and "to eat greedily, devour." The etymology of the word wolf is even more illustrative of this linguistic bias. The Greek word for wolf, *lukos*, is similar to *leukos*, meaning light, associated with Apollo, the god of reason and the patron of the shepherds (often referred to as "wolf-slayer"). The Latin word for wolf, *lupus*, is similar to *lucis*, or light. *Lucis* later became *lucem ferre*, to bear light, which, in English, became Lucifer. *Lupa*, the Latin word for female wolf, also means prostitute. The Germanic word *wargus* or *varg*, for wolf, has other connotations. Diptheria, for example, an illness that constricts the throat, was called in German *warcgingil*. An outlaw, known as a *warg*, *warag*, *weargh*, or *wearh* was an outcast, evil and damned, who dwelled in the woods like the wolf. Some philologists believe these terms derive from the nature of the wolf (at least as it was perceived by man), while others take the contrary view, that the animal received its name from the human outlaw. A similar connection between the words for wolf and words for things evil, destructive, and negative, is found in many languages. It is clear that our antipathies in relation to the wolf run so deep that in some cases the words for the animal have ceased to be neutral conveyers of meaning, and have become unconscious instruments of prejudice and further misunderstanding.

The first reference to a wolf in Western literature occurs in the *Epic of Gilgamesh*, written around 2300 B.C. by an unknown author living in the Tigris-Euphrates region, the birthplace of Western civilization. Miraculously preserved on clay tablets, and only recently discovered, it tells the story of the renowned King of Uruk in Mesopotamia and his various heroic exploits. This wolf reference, and others like it in the narrative, sets a tone that prevailed, largely unchanged, for the next five millenia:

He took arms to hunt the lion so that the shepherds could rest at night. He caught wolves and lions and the herdsmen lay down in peace, for Enkidu was their watchman, that strong man who had no rival.

(Book I, "The Coming of Enkidu")

Humankind had reached an important stage in its development: the discovery of agricultural methods sufficiently advanced to free people from the necessity of wandering incessantly in search of food. Villages and small societies, soon to be city states, were evolving side by side with irrigated croplands and domesticated ungulates. The wolf came into immediate conflict with the latter, particularly as society grew and began to reduce both the former habitat of the wolf and the wild prey base that had sustained it.

More than one thousand years later, in the epic poem *The Iliad*, the Greek poet Homer compared the Achaian soldiers fighting at the Battle of Troy to a pack of wolves:

So these lords of the Danaans killed each his own man. They as wolves make havoc among lambs or young goats in their fury, catching them out of the flocks when the sheep separate in the mountains through the thoughtlessness of the shepherd, and the wolves seeing them suddenly snatch them away, and they have no heart for fighting: so the Danaans ravaged the Trojans, and these remembered the bitter sound of terror, and forgot their furious valour.

The comparison is not altogether unfavorable. Homer has drawn a line of similarity between the valour of the warrior on the field of battle and the hunting prowess and exploits of the wolf. His fabled heroes, the "lords of the Danaans" are as adept at killing as the wolf, seen as the master of the hunt and the prey, the inept and fearful Trojans, as helpless as "lambs" or "young goats." For the first time in Western literature, through the compelling image of this extended simile, man is compared positively with the wolf. Most other classical references, whether in the Fables of Aesop, the plays of Aeschylus, the metaphors of Plato, the odes of Horace, or the Eclogues of Virgil, take the contrary and traditional view of the wolf, as an agent of terror and darkness.

Both Plutarch (*Lives of the Noble Greeks and Romans*) and Virgil (*The Aeneid*) allude to the legend of Romulus and Remus, the founders of Rome, who were, according to legend, raised in the wild by wolves:

While the infants lay there [Romulus and Remus, with Remus believed derived from *ruma*, the dug], history tells us, a shewolf nursed them . . . Others

think that the first rise of this fable came from the children's nurse, through
the ambiguity of her name; for the Latins [Plutarch's name for the forefathers
of the Romans] not only called wolves *lupae*, but also women of loose life;
and such a one was the wife of Faustulus, who nurtured these children . . .
Meantime Faustulus, Amulius's swineherd, brought up the children without
any man's knowledge.

(The Legend of Romulus)

•••••

Next Evander showed Aeneas a thick wood which the forceful Romulus was
to adopt as his "Sanctuary," and, under a dank crag, the Lupercal, the Wolf's
Cave, which is named in the Arcadian fashion after the Wolf-God, Lycaean
Pan.

(The Aeneid)

Once again, humans are seen in mythology to be like wolves; so close, in
fact, with respect to their strong social structure, nuclear family, and ritualized patterns of aggression, that some believed (or at least fantasized) that
people could be raised by wolves and become part of wolf society. Pliny
the Elder, in his *Historia Naturalis*, describes a family known as Anthus in
Arcadia, in which one person was chosen every nine years to become a
wolf and live in the wild. This is the first occurrence of what was later to
become, in Eastern Europe (and in modern cinema), the lycanthropic legend
of the wolfman or werewolf.

References to the wolf, particularly in the context of sheep, abound
in both the Old and New Testaments of the Bible. Jesus Christ often used
the wolf to illustrate his parables and stories:

Beware of false prophets, which come to you in sheep's clothing, but in-
wardly they are ravening wolves.

(St. Matthew 7:15)

•••••••

Behold, I send you forth as sheep in the midst of wolves: be ye therefore
wise as serpents, and harmless as doves.

(St. Matthew 10:16)

•••••••

I am the good shepherd: the good shepherd giveth his life for the sheep.
But he that is a hireling, and not the shepherd, whose own the sheep are
not, seeth the wolf coming, and leaveth the sheep, and fleeth . . .

(St. John 10:11–12)

Once again, the wolf is seen in the most negative terms, a bias that will
only become more deeply imbedded and institutionalized as time progresses.

Throughout the Middle Ages the once distinct living areas of humans and wolves became closer through increased human population and migration into the countryside. Forests were cleared and marshes were drained. Manors were built and a feudal system of government and society flourished. Hunting, particularly of wolves, became a favorite sport of the nobility. Under the influence of Christianity, the rational outlook of classical times was replaced by supernatural systems of thought. Wolves became synonymous with evil and the devil, and the idea of the werewolf, a legend since ancient times, now enjoyed its greatest popularity. Only once in this period do we see the wolf in something of a favorable light, and that is in *Beowulf*, the Anglo-Saxon epic in which a man with both the name and the cunning nature of a wolf vanquishes the dreaded monster Grendel, symbolic of atavism, evil, and the unknown.

With the Renaissance comes a whole proliferation of wolf references, ranging from the She-Wolf encountered by Dante as he nears the gates of Hell in *The Divine Comedy*, to the Parson's introduction in *The Canterbury Tales*, in which Chaucer uses the by-now stock comparison of parishioners to a flock of sheep threatened by a symbolic wolf. A little later, the great English playwrights of the late sixteenth and early seventeenth centuries had a distinct penchant for the wolf, a fondness probably derived from the animal's rich evocative and symbolic power. These quotes from Shakespeare are representative of those found elsewhere, in Marlowe, Webster, and Jonson:

And now loud-howling wolves arouse the jades
That drag the tragic melancholy night,
King Henry VI, Part II
4.1.2–3

•••••••

You may as well use questions with the wolf.
The Merchant of Venice
4.1.73

•••••••

'Tis like the howling of Irish wolves against the moon.
As You Like It
5.2.103

The wolf, persecuted in Great Britain as it was throughout Europe, was not found in the wild very much longer. Lord Macaulay, in his *History of England* (1848), reports that the wolves became extinct at the hand of Lochiel, a seventeenth century Scottish Highland chieftain, who made "vigorous war" on them because they "preyed on the red deer of the Grampians."

Immigrants from Europe to the New World encountered the wolf once again. They also found a group of people—the American Indians—who very often had a wholly different perspective on the wolf (and all of nature) than their own. Wolf warrior societies were commonly encountered among the Indian tribes of the High Plains, in which certain Indians, emulating the wolf packs, would constantly scout the tribal territory and protect its members against enemy attack. It was considered an honor to be a member of a "Wolf Soldier" band, and many of these warriors, particularly among the Cheyenne, put on extraordinary displays of personal heroism in battle. Farther to the west and north, among the Haida Indians of coastal British Columbia, a beautiful fable was developed that told of a time long ago when hungry wolves entered the waves in pursuit of prey and became sea wolves, the species we now know as the killer whale.

More recently, in the nineteenth century, the Russian fabulist Ivan Krilov wrote a story ("The Wolf in the Kennel"), in which a gray-coated wolf hunting a man's sheep was an allegory for the invasion of Russia by gray-coated Napoleon Bonaparte. A few years later, George Gordon, Lord Byron, in his poem "Childe Harold's Pilgrimage," made a similar analogy:

> Shall we, who struck the Lion down, shall we
> Pay the Wolf homage?

The Lion is the archetypal regal symbol, in this case of the deposed monarch of France. Bonaparte, the renegade corporal bent on forming a European empire, is described, unflatteringly, as a wolf. Elsewhere in the last century, the wolf was made the hero of Rudyard Kipling's famous Mowgli story in *The Jungle Book*, and was alluded to by Tennyson in his famous poem of Camelot *Idylls of the King* ("The Coming of Arthur"):

> And thus the land of Cameliard was waste,
> Thick with wet woods, and many a beast therein . . .
> And ever and anon the wolf would steal
> The children and devour, but now and then,
> Her own brood lost or dead, lent her fierce teat
> To human sucklings; and the children, housed
> In her foul den, there at their meat would growl,
> And mock their foster-mother on four feet,
> Till, straighten'd, they grew up to wolf-like men,
> Worse than the wolves.

The legend of the wolfman lived on, and would be resurrected again, on the silver screen, in the twentieth century.

The most interesting allusion to the wolf in our century may be in Hermann Hesse's novel *Steppenwolf*, in which a man—a loner, an alienated intellectual—is quite literally compared to a wolf:

> Harry [Steppenwolf] finds in himself a human being, that is to say, a world of thoughts and feelings, of culture and tamed or sublimated nature, and besides this he finds within himself also a wolf, that is to say, a dark world of instinct, of savagery and cruelty, of unsublimated or raw nature. In spite of this apparently clear division of his being between two spheres, hostile to one another, he has known happy moments now and then when the man and the wolf for a short while were reconciled with one another.

The philosophical conflict symbolized by man and wolf, it is now known, may have a very real biological basis. It is a conflict occurring within our brains: between the R-Complex, the ancient reptilian brain stem, seat of instinct, and impulse, and the more modern mammalian regions of the brain, the cerebral cortex and the limbic system, centers of reason and restraint.

The wolf, both as literary symbol and as living animal, will no doubt endure, not only because of its resilience and the remoteness of some of its Arctic and near-Arctic habitats, but also because humankind needs the wolf. We see in the wolf those values and traits without which we as a species will perish. A human being without a family, without roots, without work, a human being without a sense of place, of location, of community, is like a wolf without its pack, its home territory, its sense of belonging and purpose and security. The person becomes alienated, fearful, opportunistic, amoral, and, above all, alone. A society, or worse, a world, built of such people has lost its center, its heritage, and quite possibly determined its downfall. The wolf reminds us of what we cannot forget, that our origins were out there, in the cold, windy outback of time, and that we are, despite all of our homocentric pretensions, still very much a part of that wild nature.

PAST HISTORY

The wolf evolved from a specialized genus of cursorial (running) carnivore in the Paleocene era about sixty million years ago. By Miocene times, some twenty million years ago, two major carnivore families, the dogs (canids) and cats (felines), had branched from this common root, become quite distinct, and were probably recognizable as the ancestral stock of the animals that exist now. It was during the Pleistocene, approximately one million years ago, that the wolf's immediate ancestor emerged, an animal possessing a larger brain and longer nose than its predecessor, as well as specialized shearing teeth, the vestigial fifth toe on the hind leg, and the long running legs of its precursors. The wolf was possibly the parent of the domestic dog, *Canis familiaris*. Today the wolf's closest relatives among the canids are the coyote, the dingo, the jackal, and the domestic dog. The foxes and the wild dogs are more distant relatives, as are the bear, the raccoon, the marten, and the wolverine. Of them all, the wolf is clearly the most socially evolved, and many believe the most intelligent as well.

Linnaeus formally named the wolf *Canis lupus* in 1758. Since that time, thirty-two species of gray wolf have been recognized, of which twenty-four once inhabited North America. The two wolves once found in Colorado were the prairie wolf and the southern Rocky Mountain gray wolf. Both are now extinct, as are the Cascade Mountains wolf, the Texas gray wolf, the Newfoundland wolf, and the Mogollon Mountain wolf. The remaining wolves in North America are widely distributed. Both Alaska and Canada each have about ten thousand wolves, covering approximately eighty per cent of their former range and selectively harvested by trapping and hunting over most of that territory. To the south there are, at best, fifty wolves left in the Mexican states of Sonora and Chihuahua. Remnant or transient populations of six animals or less possibly exist in the border states of New Mexico, Arizona, Washington, and North Dakota. It is possible that there are equivalently small populations in remote areas in Idaho and Wyoming. Montana now has several regions along the border with Canada where wolves have recently migrated. To the east, over twelve hundred wolves are found in northern Minnesota. Around thirty wolves live in Isle Royale National Park. A smaller number of wolves inhabit the Upper Peninsula of Michigan and northern Wisconsin. A very small number of red wolves, possibly crossbred with coyotes, live in the coastal wilds of Louisiana and Texas. There are several dozen each of pure red wolves and Mexican wolves in United States captive breeding programs.

Wolves originally roamed most of the Northern Hemisphere above thirty degrees north latitude. They were found throughout Europe and Asia, from Finland south into the Mediterranean, in the Near and Middle East, the Balkans, throughout Russia, south into India and China, east into Siberia and Kamchatka, and into the northern islands of Japan. Wolves had, over one million years, adapted to every habitat in the Northern Hemisphere with the exception of the true desert. Today, the wolf has been exterminated in the British Isles, Scandinavia, and throughout most of Europe. A few wolves survive in the remote portions of the Apennine Mountains in Italy, along the French/Spanish border, and in eastern Europe. Populations in the Near and Middle East (Iran, Iraq, Israel, Afghanistan, Saudi Arabia) and in Pakistan and Northern India are critically reduced. Populations in historic Russia are thought to be relatively good, as are those in the eastern portions of the USSR. Those in China are not well known.

The ink was barely dry on the colonial charters when the first laws were passed in America to encourage the destruction of wolves. On November 9, 1630, the first wolf bounty law was passed by the Massachusetts Bay Colony. Two years later, on September 4, 1632, the Virginia Bay Colony passed a similar law. In 1697, New Jersey offered a bounty of twenty shillings for the head of a wolf. As American civilization spread over the continent, the destruction of the wolf, as well as of its habitat and prey base, continued unabated. In one state after another, the wolf disappeared. An account of the first recorded Spanish expedition into Colorado in 1719 (south and east of Pueblo along the Arkansas River) contained a reference to large bison herds, the primary prey of the native wolves. The expeditions of Lewis and Clark, Pike, and Long, all organized after the Louisiana Purchase in 1803, make mention of the ubiquitous presence of the wolf on the High Plains and in the mountains. Meriwether Lewis, June 3, 1805:

> . . . between the time of my A.M. and meridian [observation] Capt. C. [Clark] and myself stroled out to the top of the hights in the fork of these rivers from whence we had extensive and most inchanting view; the country in every direction around us was one vast plain in which innumerable herds of Buffalo were seen attended by their shepperds the wolves; the solatary antelope which now had their young were distributed over it's face; some herds of Elk were also seen . . ."

A few years later, in 1823, the traveler James O. Pattie alluded to the wolves of eastern Colorado:

> As far as the plain was visible in all direction, innumerable herds of wild horses, buffaloes, antelopes, deer, elk, and wolves, fed in their wild and fierce freedom. Here the sun rose, and set, as unobscured from the sight, as on the wastes of an ocean.

When first encountered, the wolf apparently existed in an abundance consistent with the health and size of its prey base. The young British adventurer and journalist George Frederick Ruxton was one of the first to realize that the wolf, in nature, was of some value to its prey (*Life in the Far West*, 1849):

> Dense masses of buffalo still continued to darken the plains, and numerous bands of wolves hovered around the outskirts of the vast herds, singling out the sick and wounded animals, and preying upon the calves whom the rifles and arrows of the hunters had bereaved of their mothers. The white wolf is the invariable attendent upon the buffalo; and when one of these persevering animals is seen, it is certain sign that buffalo are not far distant.

The journals of George Catlin (1841), John James Audubon (1843), and Francis Parkman (1846) make similar observations. Colorado trapper William Drannen, in his recollections, quotes Jim Bridger as saying: "If you had seen as much of (the wolf) as I have, you would know that wolves signal to each other and understand each other the same as men do." These early pioneers, like the Indians among whom they traveled, had acquired a sense of the oneness of nature and a healthy respect for the value of the wolf that would not be found in America for another hundred years.

Events slowly began to conspire on several fronts to bring about the demise of the wolf in Colorado and throughout the West. The Santa Fe Trail was opened in 1825 and was heavily used until closed by Santa Ana in 1844. Bent's Fort was built on the Arkansas River in 1832 to facilitate trade with the Arapaho and southern Cheyenne. Toward the north, the Oregon Trail brought an increasing volume of traffic through southern Wyoming, some of which began to trickle off into Colorado. So numerous were wolves at this time that human graves had to be covered with prickly pear cactus or rocks to prevent wolves from unearthing the bodies. The wolves' days, however, were numbered.

The period of 1860 to 1885 saw the major migration from east to west that would bring about the downfall of the wolf and other species. With the construction of the railroads, and particularly after the Civil War, growing numbers of people began to seek the wide open spaces and sudden fortunes that could be found west of the Mississippi. Buffalo hunters decimated the great buffalo herds that provided prey for the wolves, and concurrent with this, homesteaders began to fence and cultivate the land. Associations of woolgrowers and stockmen began to offer bounties for wolves, soon supplemented by government rewards and bounties. Professional trappers, known as "wolfers," were hired, and used poisoned bait and steel traps, particularly along wolf runways, to capture and kill the animals. One

source reports that during the winter of 1861–1862, three men trapping
along Walnut Creek in what is now Rush County, Kansas, took more than ③
three thousand wolves, coyotes, and swift foxes, a catch that brought them
twenty-five hundred dollars. Fortunes could be made in the trapping business, and were. Because wolves are such strongly social animals, it was not
uncommon for wolfers to take three to twelve wolves per day from each
carcass bait.

With the passing of the bison by 1890 and the great reductions in the
number of other wild ungulates throughout Colorado, the remaining wolves
were found only in the mountains and valleys of the Western Slope, where
they persisted somewhat longer. Steady pressure of trapping, poisoning, ④
shooting, and den-hunting, however, ultimately took their toll. Edward
Warren reported seeing a wolf on October 10, 1899 on the road between
Gothic and Schofield in Gunnison County, apparently one of the last in
that part of the state. A few of the wolves still lingered on in regional legend:
the Unaweep Wolf, of Unaweep Canyon (now in the Denver Museum of
Natural History); Bigfoot, of the Grand Junction area; the Phantom, of
Fruita; Greenhorn, of Pueblo; and Old Whitey and his mate Three Toes
of Apishapa, who lived in the Bear Springs Mesa region near Trinidad.

Across the border in New Mexico, two of the last wolves were killed
in Currumpaw County in 1894 by freelancing trapper Ernest Thompson
Seton, a pair later immortalized in his well-known story *Lobo, the King of
Currumpaw*. Colorado's best-known wolf of the period was probably "Old
Clubfoot," killed in June 1907 near the Escalante Hills in Moffat County.
Like many wolves of the period, it had lost two of its toes in a steel trap,
and subsequently left a track that was easily recognized. This wolf was reputed to be a habitual stock killer, but the number associated with it is
probably exaggerated: seventy-five head of cattle and horses. Edward Warren reports that he owned the skull in his collection, and that it was of
a "large, old animal." In 1927 possibly the last active wolf pack in Colorado, led by Old Three Toes, crossed south over the border into New Mexico
and terrorized the Carson National Forest for two years before being exterminated. A few last possible reports of sightings trickled in. During the
winter of 1932–1933, a wolf was reported about the ranch of C. F. Frey
near Maher, in Montrose County. The wolf allegedly killed and ate a portion of a domestic sheep. This wolf was not seen again after the spring of
1932. Eight wolves were reported in 1936 in the National Forests of Colorado, but by 1938 the number had fallen to just two. Ernie Wilkinson believes the last wolf in Conejos County, presumably the last native wolf in

Pictured here is Old Three Toes, probably the last wolf in Colorado. He led his small pack into northern New Mexico in 1927 and was hunted there for two years before being trapped and killed. He was a large wolf, weighing 107 pounds. Photo courtesy of David E. Brown, from his *Wolf in the Southwest* (University of Arizona Press). *J. E. Hawley*

the state, was killed in 1943. Ernie told me in August 1986 that an adult male wolf had been killed in the San Luis Valley during the winter of 1985–1986, but that it had been conclusively determined that it was a pet wolf that had escaped its enclosure.

The reasons for the decline and eventual extirpation of the wolf in Colorado are clear. First came intensive human settlement, which resulted in the destruction of both the original prey base and the original habitat of the wolf. Next came the growth of the livestock industry, which resulted in a direct conflict with the wolf. Extremely successful eradication programs were employed to remove the wolf from all parts of the state where it persisted. Along the way, the process was fueled by fears and superstitions concerning the wolf, as well as a lack of understanding about wolf ecology and the importance of predators. All of these factors, from the importance of the livestock industry to lingering myths about the wolf, persist today.

NATURAL HISTORY

For many hundreds, if not thousands, of years, man's knowledge of the wolf was confined to whatever information was necessary to trap and kill the animal. Any biological or behavioral information recorded was incidental. It is generally acknowledged that the objective scientific study of the wolf purely to increase human understanding, began with the investigations of Adolph Murie, which took place in what was then called Mt. McKinley National Park (April 1939–August 1941). The purpose of Murie's study was to determine the relationship between predation by the Alaskan wolf and the population levels of its prey, the Dall sheep. His research methods included the close observation of a wolf family during two denning seasons, the analysis of 1,174 wolf scats to determine food sources, the collection of sheep skulls and skeletal remains, the careful noting of sheep numbers, and the raising of a wolf cub captured from a wolf den. For the first time, scientists had concrete, empirical evidence of the daily regime of a wolf pack, social behavior, use of a "rendezvous site," the approximate size and shape of its home range, its food requirements, its seasonal travels, and its relationships to the other animals in the ecosystem. Perhaps most important was the fact that Murie discovered the wolf existed in equilibrium with the sheep and probably had, in his own words, "a salutary effect on the sheep as a species."

Since Murie opened the door on wolf ecology and behavior, many talented scientists have followed in his steps, notably Konrad Lorenz and his student Eric Zimen, who conducted their studies of wolf social behavior with captive animals in Germany; Douglas Pimlott in Canada; and Durward Allen and L. David Mech, who performed extensive ecological studies of wolves in Isle Royale National Park in Minnesota after the area was colonized by wolves from Canada.

As with the grizzly bear, another animal that has received unprecedented amounts of attention in the last quarter century, much more is known about the wolf than was once the case, but more still needs to be learned before we can properly manage and live with *Canis lupus*. The wolf is perhaps more threatened in some instances and in some locations than the grizzly because it is almost entirely carnivorous and preys on large ungulates, while the grizzly may in some situations be almost entirely herbivorous, and only seasonally rely on carrion or small rodents. In both cases, scientists now concentrate on acquiring information that will be useful in educating people how to coexist with the animals, and that will assist managers in establishing and/or protecting minimum viable populations.

The wolf is the largest wild member of the dog family Canidae, with adult males averaging 90 to 100 pounds (range 43–175 pounds), and adult females averaging 75 to 85 pounds (range 39–125 pounds). Wolves on the northern part of their range in North America generally weigh more than wolves on the southern parts. The largest wolf ever recorded was a 175-pound male killed on 70-Mile River in east central Alaska by a government hunter on July 12, 1939. In 1945, a Canadian park ranger killed a 172-pound wolf in Jasper National Park. Both are considered anomalies. Most wolves, even in these regions, weigh considerably less. Males are usually 5 to 6-1/2 feet in length, with females from 4-1/2 to 6 feet in length. Wolves normally stand twenty-six to thirty-two inches at the shoulder. With their long legs and deep, narrow chests, wolves are well suited for the fast and far-ranging travels necessary for their food requirements and survival. The vision of wolves is sharp and discriminating. Senses of smell and hearing are acute. Wolves can respond to other wolves howling six miles away. The digestive system has evolved to rapidly process large amounts of meat. Food is swallowed whole with little or no chewing. Digestion occurs over a period of several hours, and allows the wolf to rapidly process a prey animal. These physical attributes enable wolves to gorge themselves when a kill is made (eating meat, hide, soft tissue, connective tissue, bone marrow, and small bones), and then go without eating for several days if necessary.

The Northern Rocky Mountain Wolf Recovery Plan describes the role of the wolf in the wild:

Few animals have been as mythologized and misunderstood as the wolf. Notice the long, muscular legs and characteristically large feet of this gray wolf. *Greg Hayes*

The wolf is considerably larger than the coyote, a ubiquitous canid in Colorado, and is also better adapted to prey on the large ungulates. The presence of the wolf in Rocky Mountain National Park might help to control the burgeoning elk population. *Greg Hayes*

The wolf is well adapted for its role of preying on large ungulates. No other carnivore in Colorado performs the singular ecological function of the wolf. The coyote only sporadically preys upon ungulates. Although the mountain lion does prey on large ungulates, its ambush method of hunting and solitary ways contrast significantly with the wolf. As a result, mountain lion predation differs in the evolutionary pressure it exerts from wolf predation. The wolf does a job that no other animal in the wild can do.

Murie reported that wolf tracks can easily be distinguished from those of the coyote or the average sled dog by their large size. The front foot, normally over five inches long and four inches wide, is both broader and longer than the hind foot. Size is also relative to speed. When the wolf is loping or galloping or coursing, the foot spreads considerably, particularly in sand, mud, or shallow snow. Other sign commonly encountered include scats, which are, in an adult wolf, larger than coyote scats, and scent posts, which are frequently used by single wolves and wolf packs as a means of communicating and establishing territorial boundaries. Wolves often follow established routes as they patrol their home range and engage in opportunistic hunting, traveling along regular corridors such as game and logging trails, roads, and frozen water surfaces, occasionally cutting across country from one route to the next. One study determined that scent marking (applying body odor through rubbing) occurred every 262 yards, and raised-leg urination occurred every 492 yards. The best-known aspect of wolf natural history is probably the howl, which is used individually or collectively to signal location, establish territory, or perhaps to excite the pack prior to or after the hunt.

Wolf color and markings vary considerably from animal to animal. Marking about the face is of particular importance in communication between animals. The fur of the wolf is quite luxurious, consisting of a soft, light-colored, and extremely dense underfur that lies beneath a covering of longer guard hairs that can rapidly shed moisture and keep the fur dry and warm. The coat is thickest over the shoulders, where it forms a distinct mane, and thins out distally and over the head and muzzle. Murie's description of the differences between the individual wolves in the pack he observed in 1940 is indicative of the wide range found in the species:

> The mother of the pups was dark gray, almost "bluish," over the back, and had light under parts, a blackish face, and a silvery mane. She was thick-bodied, short-legged, short-muzzled, and smaller than the others. She was easily recognized from afar. The father was black with a yellowish vertical streak behind each shoulder. From a distance he appeared coal black except for the yellow shoulder marks, but a nearer view revealed a scattering of silver and rusty hairs, especially over the shoulders and along the sides. There was an extra fullness of the neck under the chin. He seemed more solemn than the others . . . On the hunts that I observed he usually took the lead in running down caribou calves. The other black wolf was a slender-built, long-legged female. Her muzzle seemed exceptionally long . . . What appeared to be the largest wolf was a tall, rangy male with a long silvery mane and a dark mantle over the back and part way down over the sides . . . The other gray male at the den I called "Grandpa" in my notes. He was a rangy wolf of nondescript color . . . he moved as though he were old and a little stiff . . . One of the grays that joined the group in late July was a large male with a light face except for a black robber's mask over the eyes. His chest was conspicuously white . . . The other wolf, which joined the group in August, was a huge gray animal with a light yellowish face.

Other reported shades include pure white in the Arctic regions, cream, gray, pure black, and slate blue (also in the Arctic). The wolf, like other furbearers, has been trapped solely for its pelt, which can be used for fine fur items as well as to fringe the hoods of north-country parkas and the upper portions of mukluks.

Wolf society is best described in the Rocky Mountain Wolf Recovery Plan:

> The basic unit of the wolf population is the pack, a cohesive group of two or more animals that jointly partake in all activities throughout the year. The proportion of lone wolves in established wolf populations is typically quite low, between one and fifteen per cent. The number of wolves in a pack ranges from the minimum of two to a reported high of thirty-six in Alaska. Pack size is dependent on a number of factors, including food supply, predation, natality, and the size of the prey species. Most packs include a pair of breeding adults, their pups, and often yearlings and/or extra adults. Packs form when two solitary wolves of opposite sex develop a pair bond as breeders, and produce a litter of pups.
>
> The breeding season of wolves occurs from late January through April, with wolves at the highest latitudes generally having the latest seasons. Wolf pups are born between late March and May after a sixty-three-day gestation period. Litter sizes usually range from four to seven. The size of ten wolf litters taken from dens in Yellowstone National Park earlier in this century averaged 7.8 and varied from 5 to 13. Litters of ten and eleven were found following several years of exploitation. Although females in captivity have bred at ten months of age, wild wolves normally do not breed until twenty-two months. Younger females have slightly smaller litter sizes on the average than older animals.

Two important aspects of wolf ecology, whether on the barren tundra plains of the high Arctic or in the dense coniferous forests and wet meadowlands of the Minnesota lake country, are the whelping den and the rendezvous site. The whelping den is the location where the female wolf has her litter. Dens are most commonly located on south-facing hillsides in well-drained soils, are slightly elevated from the surrounding contryside, and are fairly close to surface water. Wolves sometimes occupy natural caves or abandoned beaver lodges. Approximately six to ten weeks after the pups are born, the pack moves to a location Murie called the "rendezvous site," a specific resting and gathering place for the pack during the summer and early fall. The rendezvous site may be moved several times over the summer, but the sites are normally close together and in the same region as the natal, or whelping, den. Both the whelping den and the rendezvous sites are particularly sensitive areas and are located well away from human activity.

Many studies have been conducted of the behavioral interactions of the wolf pack. It is now apparent that wolves maintain a complex framework of hierarchical dominance based on size, strength, personality, and social roles. The central members of the pack are a dominant (alpha) male and female. Other pack members defer to these animals through various postures, facial expressions, and behavioral patterns. Aggression is channeled into ritualized behavior patterns within the social hierarchy. These roles are important to the welfare of the pack. Alpha wolves lead the pack by choosing the direction and specific routes of travel, as well as by providing leadership in hunting, and perhaps in dominating interpack encounters. Wolves apparently form buffer zones between separate packs, sometimes large neutral zones that prevent interpack conflict. Ungulates occasionally use these areas to escape predation in the home range of wolf packs.

Probably the most studied aspect of wolf ecology has been food habits. As a general rule, wolves depend upon ungulates for food in the winter and supplement this diet during the spring and fall with beaver and smaller mammals. Captive wolves have been maintained on two to three pounds of food per day. Mech proposed that a pack as a whole requires an average of at least eight pounds of meat per wolf per day during the winter for all the members to survive and for new pups to be reared successfully the following spring. How often a wolf pack kills varies tremendously, depending on the number of wolves in the pack, the weather conditions, the condition of the prey, and so on. One study reported that two wolf packs in Alberta killed moose in the winter at the rate of one moose per wolf every thirty-seven to forty-eight days.

Wolves are opportunistic predators, and will take whatever they can get, from mice to moose. In areas where there are two or more prey species, such as white-tailed deer and moose, or mule deer and elk, wolves will, as a general rule, tend to select for the smaller of the two species. Wolves also will prey on the young, the old, the infirm, or solitary rutting adult males. Hunting methods include chance encounters followed by a quick rush, often downhill, for the prey; coursing, or running a herd to separate a weak or vulnerable animal; and driving target animals toward other wolves waiting in ambush.

Finally, in wolf ecology, there is the subject of wolf mortality. Wolves die from malnutrition, parasites, disease, debilitating injuries sustained in hunting (broken skulls, legs, ribs), inter- and intra-pack strife, and human exploitation (trapping or hunting) and/or control (poisoning). Fall and winter may be critical periods for wolf survival. September appears to be a critical month for malnourished wolf pups. Mortality rates of wolf pups range broadly, depending on local situations, from twelve to eighty per cent, with rates around fifty per cent being the most common. It was found in Minnesota that wolf pups with body weights less than sixty-five per cent of standard had a poor chance of survival, while those with at least eighty per cent of standard had a high survivorship rate. Across its range, the greatest danger to the species comes from humankind.

CURRENT STATUS AND FUTURE RECOVERY

Not long ago I had the opportunity to see one of the only wolves in Colorado. No, it wasn't out on some remote alpine ridge in the Mount Zirkel Wilderness Area, or down in an obscure canyon on the Ute Indian Reservation. There are none in the wilds of Colorado anymore. It was in eastern Boulder County on the modest farm of Greg Hayes, a conservation-minded veterinarian who owns and cares for a small collection of exotic animals. In a large, immaculate enclosure near his home the doctor keeps four gray wolves. Before finishing this chapter (and this book) it seemed to me imperative to see *Canis lupus* in a little different setting than the diorama at the Denver Natural History Museum or the bloody passages of Jack London. So much has been written about the wolf, both good and bad, poetical and polemical, hysterical and historical, it seemed only fair to meet this controversial animal face to face.

I was given a six-month-old wolf pup to play with, a black-phased female gray wolf. On cursory glance she seemed like a domestic dog, resembling in a superficial way a very dark German Shepherd or Husky. But on closer examination I could see she was not a dog at all. She was something much older, much different. I was holding a bit of our past in my hands. She was a wolf, of the same species that once followed the Pawnee as they hunted bison near what we now call the Pawnee Buttes, or howled the moon up outside Bent's Fort as traders rested while making the long pull to Santa Fe. Her eyes immediately betrayed her ancestry—a sharp yellow color I have never seen in a domestic dog. Her head was larger than that of a similarly aged dog. I am told the brain of a wolf is significantly larger than that of a comparably sized dog and I can believe it. Her jaws were long and powerful looking. Most conspicuous as she played were her long legs, evolved for running (and running), and the oversized feet, already giving every promise of spanning the five inches common in adults. At times she acted like a dog, licking my face and frolicking about. At other times, though, I could detect something different, a nascent wildness. The house dogs could, too, and gave her a wide berth in the yard. With the three adults, there was no uncertainty—they were wolves. They paced as all animals meant to be in the wild paced. They longed to be free, and in their bright, intelligent eyes burned the defiant, untamed quality of the wilderness itself. As I watched them there, secure in their comfortable cages but still yearning for the independence of the open horizon, I could feel, as Steppenwolf felt, a wolf inside of me, similarly restrained, and also yearning to be free. A wolf does such things to you.

But the real question is, Do wolves belong in the wild of Colorado? Or perhaps a better question, some would say, is Do we have enough wilderness for a wide-ranging carnivore like the wolf? Nowhere in researching this book did I encounter stronger feelings, pro and con, than with the wolf. But, as we saw in the introduction, the wolf has always been at the center of controversy.

The idea of a wolf recovery in Colorado has been discussed since the passage of the Endangered Species Act in 1973. It was clear even then that the only way to remove the wolf from endangered status in Colorado would be to make provisions for reintroduction. In 1974 the Colorado Division of Wildlife stated, in a position that would eventually be reversed, that an objective for nongame management was to "provide sufficient protection and management to establish and maintain a minimum of . . . twenty gray wolves . . ." In 1976 nongame officials submitted a proposal to make a formal study of whether the reintroduction of the gray wolf and the grizzly bear might be feasible in Colorado, but this proposal (and federal grant request) were never funded or followed up. The next year the strategic plan for the Division of Wildlife specifically stated that the agency would not pursue the restoration of either species. This was further strengthened in January 1982 when the Colorado Wildlife Commission passed a formal resolution opposing the restoration of the gray wolf or the grizzly bear in Colorado.

Several officials in Rocky Mountain National Park, including Dave Stevens, the Park Biologist, have for over a decade expressed interest in restoring wolves there. The most detailed investigation on the subject so far has been the 1976 graduate thesis of Herb Conley at Colorado State University, entitled "Impacts of Reintroducing Gray Wolves into the Rocky Mountain National Park Region." Conley studied the impact of a wolf release as it would affect wildlife resources in the park and in those areas within approximately twenty-five air miles from the boundaries. He determined that there was an adequate prey base, primarily of elk and mule deer, to support between one and twenty-four wolves without depleting either population. A wolf population level above twenty-four, he concluded, would result in a decrease in the numbers of both species. He recommended that an initial release of wolves live-trapped in Alaska or Canada and transported to Colorado, consist of one mated pair with two to six young of the year. The wolves would be kept in an enclosure for an extended period of time, a period during which they would become familiar with the release area and grow accustomed to local prey species. The wolves would be instrumented and monitored after release.

Why would the National Park Service be interested in such a project? There are, according to Dave Stevens, several reasons. First, Rocky Mountain National Park, like Yellowstone National Park, is faced with the problem of burgeoning elk populations. A significant number of elk now remain inside the Park year-round, competing with the bighorn sheep and mule deer

Bighorn sheep occupy remote and often inaccessible regions in Rocky Mountain National Park, and thus would be relatively secure from wolf predation in these rocky sanctuaries. *Linda Elinoff*

for very limited winter range. A large number of elk now live all year above timberline on the fragile alpine tundra, thus negatively affecting that fragile resource. Because hunting is not permitted within a National Park, managers and researchers in the Park face a dilemma. Some believe the reintroduction of the wolf would constitute a legal and efficient way of solving the problem. The worst thing, according to Chief Park Naturalist Glen Kaye, would be to do nothing and wait for a severe winter to cause mass starvation. In a recent *Newsweek* cover story on the "Crisis in our National Parks," Glen Kaye was quoted as saying: "Sooner or later we will have a population crash, and the public has to realize what that means." No matter what the public outcry, the Park Service, in accordance with the prevailing management guidelines, will not feed the starving animals. In the meantime, the damage the ungulates may do to the range, and consequently to other species, increases.

Second, the expressed purpose of the National Park Service is to preserve ecosystems and, where necessary, to restore them to former natural conditions. The reintroduction of the wolf would thus be within the management objectives of the agency and a legitimate and legal goal to be pursued.

Third, a wolf preserve established in the Park and its surrounding environs would be a recreational attraction, as it is in Isle Royale National Park in Michigan, Abruzzo National Park in Italy, or Bialowieza Forest in Poland. Wolves pose no threat to the public – as the renowned biologist L. David Mech wrote in his definitive book *The Wolf*, "There is no basis for the belief that healthy, wild wolves in North America are of any danger to human beings." The wolf would be considered a recreational resource by park officials, and at the same time a valuable game management tool.

There are a number of issues raised by the consideration of this alternative for Rocky Mountain National Park. The chief concern among opponents of this plan is for livestock. The wolf is a natural enemy of domesticated livestock, whether sheep, cattle, or horses. The wolf is also a widely roaming animal, known to cover great distances and have a large home range (whose size depends on prey density and availability). This is not a particularly good time for the livestock industry in Colorado. Meat consumption is down. Many ranchers have folded in the nationwide trend of foreclosures. Also, many Colorado woolgrowers were hurt – even wiped out – by blizzards in 1984 and 1985. These blizzards either trapped sheep on their alpine and subalpine range or struck shortly after they had been sheared, resulting in tremendous loss of life. To bring up an issue as volatile as wolf restoration at this time is, to many, unthinkable. It would be another bitter blow

Elk are found throughout Rocky Mountain National Park and would serve as the primary prey of the wolf if they were to be reintroduced there. In the Canadian Rockies, wolves prey upon rut-weakened bulls. *John Murray*

from a distant and uncaring government. Woolgrowers worry about having to document wolf kills and then go through a time-consuming process to get reimbursed for losses. Cattlemen are not as worried about wolves as are the woolgrowers, but many ranchers run both cattle and sheep on their titled land and on their grazing allotments. The differences between the two groups are no longer as great as they once were. Finally, livestock representatives argue that people in the city simply don't understand what it is like to work the land and to raise domesticated animals. To woolgrowers, it isn't simply a matter of getting paid for the damage that a wolf might do to their livestock. Particularly in the smaller outfits, ranchers and their families grow attached to their animals. In many cases, a small rancher might be able to look out over his herd and tell you something about every animal. He might have helped this cow give birth, or saved that lamb from a blizzard. To lose that animal to depredation would be more than an economic loss—it would be a personal loss. Having lived in rural southwestern Colorado, and seen the kind of damage coyotes can do to sheep (not very often to cattle), I can sympathize with the concerns of the livestock industry

Mule deer would also be preyed upon by wolves in Rocky Mountain National Park. In northern Minnesota, where both moose and white-tailed deer are present, wolves sometimes select for the smaller species. *John Murray*

over the wolf. It would not be suitable to relocate the wolf in any area where there is intensive livestock grazing.

Officials in the Division of Wildlife and on the Colorado Wildlife Commission oppose the reintroduction of the wolf for a number of reasons. First, the state of Colorado already pays out more in compensation for game damage than any other state. Last year payments were in excess of $750,000. The state pays for damage done to livestock by black bears and lions, as well as crop damage done by antelope, deer, and elk. The agency simply does not want to have to put out another eighteen thousand dollars a year for wolf depredations (a figure paid by Minnesota in recent years). Second, there is the question of how our wildlife funds are best spent. How can we get the greatest benefit to the most people for the dollar spent—in purchasing some essential prairie chicken habitat or in putting a radio collar on a gray wolf? Third, there is the conviction that the wolf has the best chance in the areas in which it currently is found—primarily Canada and Alaska. Many officials who oppose the reintroduction of the wolf are conservationists whose real concern is for the wolves—they wouldn't want a wolf to be illegally trapped, poisoned, or hunted in Colorado when it could be running free in Denali National Park. If the wolf were found only in Colorado—as, for example, the endangered squawfish—then they would bite the bullet and make the concessions—and do everything they could for it. But the fact is, the wolf is doing fine elsewhere. So why, they say, bring it here? Our money and time is better spent elsewhere. Besides, they say, we don't have an area large and wild enough for wolves.

Proponents of the restoration of wolves in Rocky Mountain National Park respond with equally interesting arguments. First, they say, with regard to livestock depredations, there is little or no livestock grazing in any of the counties near the National Park: Boulder, Grand, Jackson, or Larimer. I checked with the Colorado Woolgrowers Association and found this is true—the closest areas of intensive livestock grazing are fifty to seventy miles to the west, in the Yampa River, White River, and Colorado River country. Proponents believe livestock depredations would be minimal and could be carefully controlled by a zone management system and a payment plan for documented kills. In the zone management system, as is used for grizzlies in Yellowstone National Park, the park would provide an area of more or less complete protection for the wolves. Roughly concentric areas around the park would give managers greater flexibility in dealing with problem wolves, including removing the wolf from the population. A payment plan would give the owner a fair market price for any losses incurred, as, for example, Alberta does for wolf damage in its province, or the World Wildlife Fund and the Italian Government do for wolf damage in areas around Abruzzo National Park. It is also possible a conservation organization could match the market price, thus doubling the compensation the livestock owner receives. This would give the livestock interests a reason not to quietly kill marauding wolves, and would prevent marginal operations from going under because of isolated depredations. Still, all agree that livestock depredations would occur and would be a seasonal problem, particularly in the crucial late-summer period when the young of the year must put on sufficient weight to survive the lean winter months.

There have been a number of scientific studies on wolf ecology as it relates to livestock depredations. One area in the United States that has been intensely studied is northern Minnesota, where it is estimated there are about twelve hundred wolves. Keep in mind with these figures that less than thirty wolves are envisioned for the park transplant—any excess would have to be trapped and removed. First of all, there is a big difference between northern Minnesota and northcentral Colorado. There are over

In his graduate thesis on wolf restoration in Rocky Mountain National Park, Herb Conley recommended the headwaters of Forest Canyon, seen here, as a location for the wolf enclosure. Although Forest Canyon may be too close to heavily-traveled Trail Ridge Road for such an enclosure, it is historic summer range for the Big Thompson elk herd. *John Murray*

Perhaps a more appropriate place for a wolf enclosure would be the headwaters of Hague Creek, as pictured here from the alpine ridgeline south of Mummy Pass. All of what is shown here, except for the distant peaks at center and to the north, is in Rocky Mountain National Park. The Hague Creek area is a cross-country zone in which there are no developed trails or camping sites. Visitor use is extremely low. *John Murray*

300,000 head of sheep and cattle on some 12,000 farms in Minnesota's wolf country. The area is *much* more heavily grazed than the area around Rocky Mountain National Park (there is no grazing in the park). Despite the fact that there is a heavy population of sheep and cattle in this area of dense wolf population, it was found that in any given year only about one-fifth of one per cent of those farms lost even one animal to wolves. In most of these cases it was determined that poor husbandry practices contributed to wolf depredations. Even at chronic sites it was found that losses were sporadic, that wolf problems were localized, and that few wolves were involved. Where wolves did prey on sheep and cattle it was determined, not surprisingly, that they select for sheep over cattle, and select for calves and yearlings over cows and bulls. Again, husbandry practices were found either to contribute to or prevent incidents.

From 1979–1981, greatest single-year losses in northern Minnesota were 30 cattle and 110 sheep in 1981. About ten per cent of the annual complaints involved coyotes. Only a few farms and grazing leases sustained more than one wolf depredation during any one grazing season. Nevertheless, at a few farms in Minnesota, multiple incidents have occurred. The number of farms in the study period that suffered verified losses to wolves averaged twenty-two, with a range of twelve to thirty-eight. Often, only a single farmer sustained serious losses. In 1977, for example, one sheep farm received sixty-five per cent of the total compensation paid out by Minnesota for that year. In 1978, a single cattle ranch received forty-two per cent, and the same ranch was paid fifty-one per cent of the total the following year. Minnesota paid up to four hundred dollars per animal on verified wolf kills or injuries during this period. From 1977 through 1980, the state Department of Agriculture paid farmers a total of $72,381.82 on eighty-six of ninety-three claims. On the average, about $18,100 per year was paid to sixteen farmers for twenty-one claims, or an average of $865 per claim. Capture and removal reduced losses at some farms and grazing leases.

Proponents observe that because Colorado would have less than thirty wolves, that there is little livestock grazing in the environs of Rocky Mountain National Park, and that there is a sufficient prey base inside the park for the wolves, livestock depredations cannot be used as a reason not to import and release the wolves. They argue that it would simply not be that big of a problem. If the wolves were to be released in the San Juans, where there is extensive use of the National Forest for sheep grazing, there would be a problem. There would also be a problem if the wolves left the park entirely and drifted down the Colorado River into the White River country, where there are a lot of sheep. The wolves, however, would have radio collars on and could be captured long before they got into mischief. In fact, they could be outfitted with a new form of radio collar that contains an anesthetic dart that can be activated to immobilize the animal for easy capture. Technology could help, proponents argue, in making what was unthinkable ten years ago possible now.

Furthermore, they argue, the possible restoration of gray wolf in the park should be seen in a larger national and international context. The 1986 revised version of the Northern Rocky Mountain Wolf Recovery Plan proposes that the wolf be restored in three areas: 1) Northwestern Montana in and around Glacier National Park; 2) Northwestern Wyoming in and around Yellowstone National Park; and 3) Central Idaho in and around the Selway-Bitterroot Wilderness Area. Because the natural colonization of these last two areas is a remote, if not impossible scenario, plans have been made to translocate wolves into them. The 1982 Amendments to the 1973 Endangered Species Act contain specific provisions for the reintroduction of endangered or threatened species into areas they formerly inhabited. These populations are referred to as "experimental populations," existing when "the population is wholly separated geographically from nonexperimental populations of the same species." These experimental populations can be created "outside the current range of such species if the Secretary (of the Interior) determines that such release will further the conservation of such species." Experimental populations are further subdivided into nonessential and essential experimental populations. The wolves of Rocky Mountain National Park would fall in the former category. Their preservation would not be essential to the conservation of the species. They would be reintroduced for another purpose, to keep the elk numbers down and restore natural selection to the populations upon which they prey.

Additionally, proponents point to North Carolina, where red wolves are being released on the 118,000-acre Alligator River National Wildlife Refuge, and to the southwestern United States, where the U.S. Fish and Wildlife Service is studying areas in Arizona, New Mexico, and Texas for the release of captive-bred Mexican wolves. A wolf restoration in Rocky Mountain National Park, they argue, should be seen in this contemporary perspective, and not judged by the standards of the past. There is, they say, an increasing public awareness of the value of predators, and a growing acceptance of the importance of their role in nature. People in crowded south Florida have learned to contend with ten-foot bull alligators on their golf courses, and speed bumps every fifty yards in the Everglades help save the endangered panther. People in Montana have learned to stay away from trails where the grizzlies come down to graze in the early spring. While the old views still prevail in many quarters, there is a fresh new breeze blowing across the land as well. What was once an impossible scenario is now, if not likely, at least open to reasonable discussion.

Rocky Mountain National Park is not as large a park as Glacier or Yellowstone. Like them, it preserves only a portion of a larger integrated ecosystem. On first glance, it does not look sizable enough to accommo-date wolves: there are only four hundred square miles in the park. It is, however, surrounded almost completely by three National Forests (Arapa-hoe, Roosevelt, and Routt). In those National Forests are six small- to medi-um-sized wilderness areas (Never Summer, Neota, Comanche Peak, Indian Peaks, Rawah, and Cache la Poudre). There is also an extremely large 70,000-acre State Forest nearby, Colorado State Forest. All totaled, there are over eight hundred square miles of public land, including the four hundred square miles within the park, in which the wolves might find suitable habitat. The wolf restoration areas up north average around three thousand square miles, but it must be remembered that authorities are talking about a hundred or so wolves in those areas. Rocky Mountain National Park would only have twenty or thirty wolves in it. A logical release point for the wolves would be the isolated Hague Creek-Desolation Peaks region in the Mummy Range, an area in which there are presently no developed trails and little backcountry use. This would be a superior location to Forest Canyon, the area recommended by Conley in his thesis, because it is more remote and there are also a large number of elk in the area. Biologists like Dave Stevens argue the park is sufficiently large to accommodate the small number of wolves planned to be released. Surplus wolves could be removed from the population and put into captivity.

Any plan for wolf recovery in Rocky Mountain National Park will have to address the concerns of a number of affected groups: woolgrowers, cattle-men, big-game hunters, hikers, fishermen, local residents. Such a proposal will also have to convince the Colorado Wildlife Commission and the Divi-sion of Wildlife of the suitability of such an effort in Colorado. Any de-cision will have to take into account a number of factors, not the least of which is how our money is best spent. On first glance, the wolves would seem a costly project (and a management-intensive project). It must be re-membered, however, that the animals would, in a sense, be getting paid to do a job. They would be reintroduced not so much for reasons of ethics or aesthetics, but because they would keep the elk numbers down to an acceptable level in the park.

Will there ever be wolves in Colorado outside of Dr. Hayes's enclosure and other such places? Skeptics say no, not now or in the future. They argue that there is not enough wild land and that we should concentrate our efforts where they will do the most good. These same people might accept a wolverine or a lynx recovery in the park, but would oppose a wolf recovery there. The optimists believe there is a chance—not a great chance, but still a chance—to bring the wolf into the park. They concede the difficulties, but point to the alternative—excessive numbers of elk doing damage to one of our crown-jewel national parks. They observe that there was much opposition to the importation of the Yellowstone elk in Colorado after the indigenous Merriam's elk was hunted into extinction in the early part of the century. Ranchers were afraid the elk would eat them out of house and home (which they almost do in some areas each winter). But people insisted the elk be restored, and it was. More recently, the Shiras or Yellowstone moose was released in North Park, much to the consternation of many of the local residents. Over some pretty vocal opposition, the moose was restored and is now doing so well we can hunt them. I have even been told that some of the residents who most strongly objected to the moose project are now glad it was done. They enjoy watching the moose during the winter when they yard up near the river in front of their homes.

Might the same happen with the gray wolf? Probably not for a while, but it is not impossible. I think Bob Ralston, the Executive Vice President of the Colorado Cattlemen's Association, put it best. The problem with the reintroduction of species like the wolf or grizzly, he observed, is not so much a problem of people and animals, it is a problem of people and people. It is a situation in which a lot of people with different backgrounds and interests and livelihoods will have to sit down together and talk, and, most importantly, listen. It may be that the wolf will not be returned to Colorado, but it probably is something, given the interest expressed by responsible officials in Rocky Mountain National Park, that should be more seriously examined than it has been. As with the wolverine, lynx, and grizzly, it will probably be necessary to form a private, non-profit organization devoted exclusively to wolf restoration for it to gain any real momentum. Such a group, as with the grizzly, will have to brace themselves for a long and difficult battle.

The Ute Indians called it Haquihana or Wolf Valley because of its many wolves. Today we call it the North Fork of the Colorado River and its upper valley lies entirely within the boundaries of Rocky Mountain National Park. There has not been a wolf track across its snows in seventy winters. If conservationists work conscientiously and meet with success, perhaps the wolf will once again roam this valley. Perhaps one day a pair of cross-country skiers will stop on the Lulu City trail and listen to an eerie howl as it echoes through the cold January forests. Perhaps one will turn to the other and ask, "What was all the fuss about?"

The wolf is one of the most intelligent predators, and shows many of the social behaviors also found in humans. *Greg Hayes*

IX

THE YEARS TO COME

We are continually faced with a series of great opportunities, brilliantly disguised as insoluble problems.

—John Gardner, *Excellence*

In the alder grove it was cool, almost cold, and I quickly forgot how hot it had been out on the river all afternoon. I laid my fly rod down in the grass, stepped out of the badly leaking chest waders, and put on the old tennis shoes. It had not been a good day for fishing. My friend had caught and released eleven good-sized trout. I had raised only a few elusive strikes and hidden snags. I sat there for a while, feeling almost chilled in the deep shade, watching the river flow a few feet away, and hearing the splash of trout rising in the pool I had just worked for an hour. We were fishing the Colorado River below Rocky Mountain National Park, where it winds lazily through the wide flood plain between the mountains. It was September and the hay fields were all cut, the hay stacked ten bales high behind the tall elk fences. Up higher the aspen groves formed bright golden patterns and streaks on the dark coniferous ridges. Above the hills were the peaks, as old as the rivers and full of scars, deceptively close in the clear light of the late afternoon. There was not a single cloud in all the sky.

On such a day there is a quality of sadness in the air, of spent fertility and loss, and yet, too, there is the sense of contentment, of fruition and completion, that always crowns the end of a season.

I watched two hawks above the ridge across the river as they steadied themselves on an updraft, holding their outstretched wings perfectly still before shifting their position a few feet. They could hold a position longer than seemed possible. Finally one of them dropped into the sagebrush and rose up with some kind of small rodent. They flew off together out of sight and I turned to take the trail back through the forest to the end of the road.

Midway through the forest I stopped. A squirrel sprinted over to the base of a towering, narrow-leafed cottonwood, looked around nervously for a moment, and then quickly buried a pine cone. Somewhere nearby a mourning dove cooed softly. At my feet a tiny brown spider labored over an immense and beautiful web, spun between two long blades of grass. I had to see the river one more time before returning to the city.

I followed the river past the last pool I had fished and crossed over into some property I didn't know anything about. It was at the mouth of the first irrigation ditch, near the closed gate to the dry browning fields, that I found the tracks. There were many of them scattered around what had been, a few hours earlier, the whole body of a living trout. All that remained now was the head and the back and some scales shining silver from the light in the sky. The otter had eaten almost the entire fish, and had left its distinctive webbed tracks with the sharp claw imprints all over the mud and the sand. The tracks told the story. The trout had been trapped in the little pool between the closed gate and the low river. The otter had found it there, probably while I had been fishing around the bend.

I looked up toward the high peaks along the Continental Divide, catching the last red light of the day. So they come this far down the river, I thought. How about that? For a moment I took preservation very personally. At least it had made one unlucky fisherman happy for a few moments. I walked back empty-handed and smiling along the river as the swallows began to dip and swerve over the last hatch of the day.

Even there, in the microcosm of Middle Park, two hours west of Denver, the massive changes being wrought in Colorado in our time are evident. Fifty-car coal trains thunder through Byers Canyon carrying Western Slope coal to Front Range power plants. A lumber plant in Kremmling spews forth clouds of smoke as it converts aspen groves and pine forests into waferboard and lumber to be used building new homes in Douglas, Arapahoe, and El Paso counties. A new dam backs the Colorado River up a few miles west of Granby. Toxic wastes are carried cross-country on eighteen-wheelers rumbling along U.S. 40. Ski resorts and associated developments in the southern part of Grand County expand more each year, engulfing winter range for deer and elk. Elsewhere in the county, prime agricultural land is being lost to other new developments, following a statewide trend. Rocky Mountain National Park continues to see as many annual visitors as does Yellowstone, a park six times its size. If a tunnel is built under Berthoud Pass, it will see even more use. Overhead jets power down as they begin their final descent toward one of the busiest airports in the world. At night satellites designed and built in Colorado speed through the stars. And yet, in the midst of this unprecedented change, the river otter is brought back, released, and survives.

That to me is the common theme in this book: the dilemma of how to balance preservation and development. Growth is here to stay, but so is conservation. How do we reconcile the two? Is it possible to make (or remake) a world in which beauty and business can coexist, in which there is a place for fifty-story skylines and species like the river otter? That is the challenge of our time, the unlikely marriage of two strange bedfellows: capitalism and conservation.

State wildlife researcher Tom Beck made some interesting points in his notes on this manuscript. He observed, for example, that we need to re-member that there are limits to what we can do sometimes to help endangered species:

> Isn't it amazing that this relict population [the black-footed ferrets at Mee-teetse] flourished unknown to science with no concern for "diversity of genetic material," and did just fine until we started managing them? Sometimes we are the worst, most powerful enemy, in search of academic answers.
>
> •••••••
>
> How about the lesson of humility: perhaps man cannot save everything with a technological fix, an investment of money. Sometimes we need to let the beasts loose, to do as they will. We can help from the sidelines, but when we decide to be quarterback we don't always know the plays.

It is easy to forget that we may be attempting the impossible when our guilt demands that we try at all costs to rectify the wrongs of civilization.

While it is true that there are limitations and that they need to be re-membered, it is also true that there is still much of value that can be done. Although otters will probably never again swim at the confluence of Cherry Creek and the South Platte River near downtown Denver, they will proba-

"When I looked up, my heart stood still, as the books say. About 150 feet ahead were three grizzlies. They reared up, one after the other. . . They stood for a moment and then got down on their four legs and disappeared into the willows."—Bob Marshall, *Alaska Wilderness* (1939). *William Ervin*

bly do quite well elsewhere in the state, in habitats like the Black Canyon
of the Gunnison River or the Dolores River. Both the wolverine and the
lynx could probably manage to find suitable habitat in Rocky Mountain
National Park, or elsewhere if it could be demonstrated there would be no
adverse impact on other activities. The wolf and grizzly are long shots by
any oddsmaker, but it is not impossible that one day society will change
to the extent that they can be returned. The jury is still out on the black-
footed ferret, and probably will be for quite some time.

With the endangered animals in this book, and with endangered animals and plants elsewhere, I believe societies are measured as mountaineers
are, by the difficulty of the agenda they establish for themselves—the goals,
either lofty or little, by which they test themselves. I believe a reasonable
goal with the six endangered mammals of Colorado would be to find at
least one suitable location in the state where each could be returned and
maintained as a viable population in perpetuity. Not only would they be
living indicators of the integrity of their habitats, but they would also be
visible reminders of our commitment to keeping the wilderness of Colorado truly wild. These natural areas will provide a much needed buffer zone
between individuals and their stressful world in the crowded centuries that
will follow our own. The preservation of these endangered mammals will
establish Colorado as a leader in nongame wildlife management, both regionally and nationally, and will, I hope, inspire neighboring states to similar
endeavors.

In the case of the wolverine, lynx, grizzly bear, and wolf, it will probably be necessary for private groups to direct and organize the effort to win
approval for restoration. Perhaps an umbrella group—a "Colorado Endangered
Species Society"—could oversee the specialized efforts to restore the individual species; or perhaps it would be better to simply have a group of single-
purpose organizations. In any event, it is certain that nothing will happen
unless and until a group of people sharing a common preservation philosophy
and a sophisticated political sense organize themselves and their resources.
Furthermore, these preservationists must realize that other animals—the
"species of special concern" mentioned in the preface—may and probably
will become threatened or endangered in Colorado in the future. It is a
challenge that will persist so long as human civilization endures.

Similarly, private organizations would be beneficial to efforts to form
a Short Grass National Park or Preserve in northeastern or southeastern
Colorado, to establish a South San Juan National Park in southwestern Colorado, or to purchase the Banded Peak ranch for use as a state or national

park. As with the organizations convened to work for the individual animals, these groups would need to focus on fund-raising, public education, and forming the coalitions necessary to win approval for their proposals. Will any of this ever happen? Perhaps, but only if these kindred souls unite and show determination. That quintessential American philosopher, Ralph Waldo Emerson, as usual, said it best: "Every reform was once a private opinion."

The sun had dropped behind the western mountains by the time we reached the paved road. The fire had gone out of the contrail of a cross-country DC-10 and a crescent moon was hanging off its starboard wing. In the last light below I could see a coyote brazenly pouncing on field mice beside a hay stack not fifty yards from a ranch house. Nearby some mule deer were grazing in among the Hereford cattle and quarter horses. Some black ravens rose from the stubble field, banked widely against the last blue of the sky, and settled into the leafless branches of an immense alder. Soon the cold front predicted on the radio would arrive. It would snow in the high country and the cirque lakes would freeze over and another season would be gone.

After many such seasons this generation will be returned to the Earth, repaying the debt incurred by every carbon-based organism at birth. What posterity will write about us, either good or bad, will depend a lot on you, the reader of this book: on how you think, with whom you converse, where you make your donations, and, perhaps most important in a democracy, for whom you vote. The endangered mammals described in this book will not be helped much unless a lot of people care for them and act on their convictions. Above all, we must save habitat. That begins with each of us.

At the conclusion of *On Aggression*, a sobering work on animal behavior that finds aggression a pervasive and dark truth of nature on earth, the ethologist Konrad Lorenz manages an optimistic statement:

> I believe in the power of human reason, as I believe in the power of natural selection. I believe that reason can and will exert a "selection pressure" in the right direction.

If reason prevails, as Lorenz believes it will, so will the wilderness and so will the wild creatures. And so, ultimately, will we.

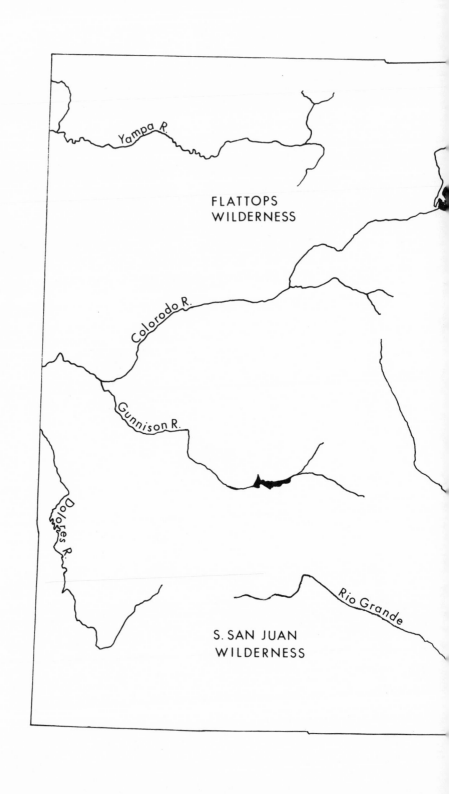

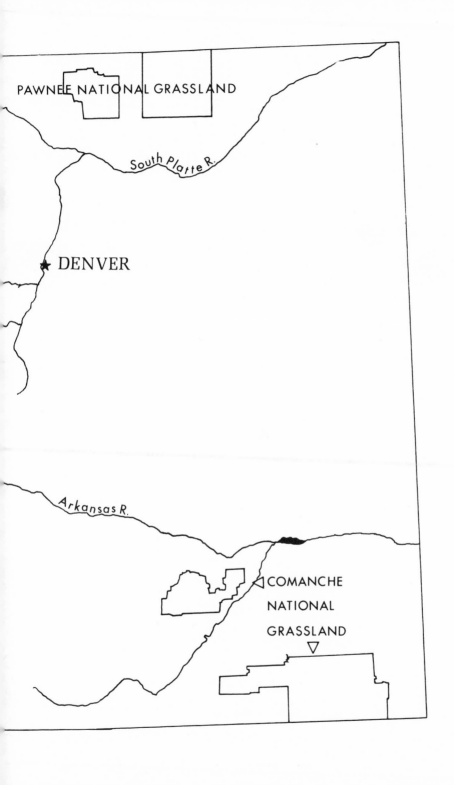

Glossary

Carrying capacity: The biomass available in a given area to support a species (e.g., browse for deer; prey for wolves).

Conspecific: Of the same species.

Cover: Cover is an important component of mammalian habitat and consists of those vegetated regions in which the animal is obstructed from view. It is valued in terms of its size, density, and location.

Critical habitat: The specific area essential to the conservation of a fish, wildlife, or plant species, and which may require special management considerations or protection under the Endangered Species Act (ESA) of 1973.

Delist: To completely remove a species from ESA Endangered or Threatened status because of successful recovery efforts.

Dispersal: The scattering of animals that sometimes occurs after they have been reintroduced or translocated into a new region, a behavior that often exposes them to greater man-induced mortality.

Downlist: To move a species from one ESA classification to another; to reclassify from Endangered to Threatened status, or from Threatened to Delisted status.

Endangered: Any species that is in danger of extinction throughout all or a significant portion of its range.

Endangered Species Act of 1973: A Congressional Act passed in 1973 and amended in 1982 that greatly expanded federal regulatory authority with respect to Endangered Species, as had already been delineated in the Endangered Species Preservation Act of 1966 and the Endangered Species Conservation Act of 1969. The Act was an extremely strong, comprehensive, and prohibitive statement of federal policy to be implemented by the Secretary of the Interior, and represented the culmination of seventy years of steadily advancing federal wildlife law.

Extinct: Said of a species of fish, wildlife, or plant that no longer exists anywhere on the earth.

Extirpated: Said of a species of fish, wildlife, or plant that has been eliminated on a portion of its range, but that can still be found somewhere in the wild (e.g., the wolf is extirpated in Colorado, but can still be found in Minnesota).

Heterozygous: An animal or plant containing genes for *both* members of at least one pair of allelomorphic characters (an allelomorph, or allele, consists of either of a pair of alternative Mendelian characters).

Home range: A term applied to the living area of a species, sometimes determined by the "cruising radius" of observed individuals. It must contain all of the species' requirements—food, cover, and water—for both sexes, all age classes, all seasons, and all activities.

Homozygous: An animal or plant containing either but *not both* members of at least one pair of allelomorphic characters (an allelomorph, or allele, consists of either of a pair of alternative Mendelian characters).

Hydric: A term applied by ecologists to stand types characterized by moist environment (e.g., the aspen stand was thirty meters from the stream in a "hydric" soil).

Management: To provide direction with which to use, control, enhance, or protect a species and/or its habitat.

Mesic: A term applied by ecologists to stand types that are neither wet (hydric) nor dry (xeric) (e.g., the ponderosa stand was interspersed with "mesic" components).

Minimum viable population: The smallest population having a ninety-five per cent chance of remaining extant for one hundred years despite the foreseeable effects of known circumstances.

Morphology: A branch of biology that deals with the form and structure of plants and animals; the features comprised in the form and structure of an organism or any of its parts.

Natality den: The location at which parturition, or birth, occurs.

Phenology: A branch of biology dealing with the relations between climate and periodic biological phenomena, particularly of the relation of plant growth and development to climate.

Phylogeny: The history of a kind of organism; the evolution of a genetically related group of organisms as distinguished from the development of the individual organism.

Prey biomass: The total weight of living organisms in an area that constitute prey for a given predator; the total weight of primary species and important secondary species in a given area.

Recovery: Natural and/or assisted increase to specific minimum viable population levels established by the designated recovery team pursuant to the Endangered Species Act of 1973; complete delisting.

Relict population: An insular remnant population isolated from other populations in the historic range; usually with no free natural corridors to genetically revitalize or otherwise augment the population.

Rendezvous site: A gathering site for members of a wolf pack used primarily for pup rearing during the summer, and occasionally for security during the fall or early winter.

Reintroduction: The Endangered Species Act of 1973, as amended in 1982, contains specific provisions for the translocation or reintroduction of threatened or endangered species outside the current range of such species "if the Secretary (of the Interior) determines that such release will further the conservation of such species."

Ruminant: Of or relating to the suborder (Ruminantia) of even-toed hoofed animals (e.g., deer, elk, sheep, moose, antelope, goats) that chew cud and have a complex three- or four-chambered stomach.

Species: Any group of fish or wildlife having common attributes and having a common name, that interbreed when mature.

Species requirement: The physical and biological requirement of an organism for adaptation, survival, and reproduction.

Taxonomy: The orderly classification of life according to presumed natural relationships.

Threatened: Any species that could become endangered in the foreseeable future throughout all or a significant portion of its range.

Whelping den: The natality site for wolves; the place where pups are born.

Ungulate: Any of a group (Ungulata) consisting of the hoofed mammals and including the ruminants, most of which are herbivorous and have horns.

Xeric: A term applied by ecologists to dry stand types.

Zone management concept: A wildlife management concept by which management priority and concern is deemphasized beyond a central core area offering total protection.

Appendix:
Organizations Involved with
Endangered Species

After reading a book like this, many people wonder how they can help, whether locally or globally. The following organizations are a few actively involved in the effort to help endangered species.

American Association for the Advancement of Science (AAAS): 1515 Massachusetts Avenue N.W., Washington, D.C. 20005. *Science* (weekly)

American Museum of Natural History: Central Park West at 79th Street, New York, N.Y. 10024. *Natural History* (monthly)

American Society of Mammalogists: Secretary-Treasurer, Section of Mammals, Carnegie Museum of Natural History, 4400 Forbes Avenue, Pittsburgh, Pa. 15213. *Journal of Mammalogy* (quarterly)

Audubon Society: 950 Third Avenue, New York, N.Y. 10022. *Audubon* (bimonthly), *American Birds* (bimonthly), *Nature Center News* (quarterly), *Audubon Action* (quarterly)

Defenders of Wildlife: 2000 N Street N.W., Washington, D.C. 20036. *Defenders* (bimonthly)

Environmental Defense Fund: 475 Park Avenue South, New York, N.Y. 10016. *EDF Letter* (bimonthly)

Environmental Law Institute: 1346 Connecticut Avenue N.W., Washington, D.C. 20036. *Environmental Law Reporter* (monthly)

Environmental Policy Center: 327 C Street S.E., Washington, D.C. 20003.

Friends of the Earth: 529 Commercial Street, San Francisco, Calif. 94111. *Not Man Apart* (biweekly)

Great Bear Foundation: P.O. Box 2699, Missoula, Mont. 59806. *Bear News* (quarterly)

Greenpeace USA: P.O. Box 4793, Santa Barbara, Calif. 93103. *The Greenpeace Examiner* (quarterly)

International Union for the Conservation of Nature and Natural Resources: 1196 Gland, Switzerland. *IUCN Bulletin* (bimonthly); *Red Data Books* (from Species Survival Commission); *TRAFFIC Bulletin* (from Wildlife Trade Monitoring Unit, 219c Huntingdon Road, Cambridge CB3 0DL, U.K., bimonthly)

National Geographic Society: 1145 17th Street N.W., Washington, D.C. 20036. *National Geographic* (monthly); *Research Reports* (annual)

National Parks and Conservation Association: 1701 18th Street N.W., Washington, D.C 20009. *National Parks and Conservation Association Magazine* (monthly)

National Wildlife Federation: 1412 16th Street N.W., Washington, D.C. 20036.

Natural Resources Defense Council, Inc.: 15 W. 44th Street, New York, N.Y. 10036. *Amicus* (quarterly); *NRDC News* (quarterly)

The Nature Conservancy: 1800 N. Kent Street, Arlington, Va. 22209. *News* (bimonthly)

North American Association for the Preservation of Predatory Animals: Box 161, Doyle, Calif. 96109.

River Otter Fellowship: Box 20611, Irwindale, Calif. 91706. *Brightwater Journal*

Sierra Club: 530 Bush Street, San Francisco, Calif. 94108. *Sierra Club Bulletin* (monthly); *National News Report* (weekly)

Smithsonian Institution: Washington, D.C. 20560. *Research Reports* (quarterly); *Smithsonian* magazine (monthly)

Wild Canid Survival Research Center (Wolf Sanctuary): P.O. Box 20528, St. Louis, Mo. 63139. *Bulletin* (quarterly); *Alerts* (as needed)

Bibliography

Chapter I: Endangered Species: An Introduction

Allen, Thomas B. 1974. *Vanishing wildlife of North America*. Washington, D.C.: National Geographic Society.

Bean, Michael J. 1977. *The evolution of wildlife law*. Council on Environmental Quality. Washington, D.C.: U.S. Government Printing Office.

Colinvaux, P. 1979. *Why big fierce animals are rare: an ecologist's perspective*. Princeton: Princeton University Press.

Day, David. 1980. *The doomsday book of animals*. New York: Viking Press.

Drabelle, Dennis, and Nathaniel P. Reed. 1983. *The United States Fish and Wildlife Service*. Boulder, Colo.: Westview Press.

Ehrlich, Paul, and Anne Ehrlich. 1980. *Extinction: the causes and consequences of the disappearance of species*. New York: Random House.

Einstein, Albert. 1950. *Out of my later years*. New York: The Philosophical Library.

Fisher, James, and Prince Philip, Duke of Edinburgh. 1970. *Wildlife crisis*. New York: Cowles Book Company.

Florio, Pier L., and Francesco B. Salvadori. 1978. *Rare and beautiful animals*. New York: Newsweek Books.

Hornaday, William T. 1913. *Our vanishing wildlife: its extermination and preservation*. New York: Scribners.

Leopold, Aldo. 1966. *A Sand County almanac, with essays on conservation from Round River*. New York: Oxford University Press.

Matthiessen, Peter. 1959. *Wildlife in America*. New York: Viking Press.

Milne, Lorus, and Margery Milne. 1971. *The cougar doesn't live here anymore*. Englewood Cliffs: Prentice-Hall.

Nilsson, Greta. 1982. *The endangered species handbook*. New York: The Animal Welfare Institute.

Stewart, Daryl. 1981. *From the edge of extinction, the fight to save endangered species.* New York: Methuen.

Time-Life. 1976. *Vanishing species.* New York: Time-Life Books.

Trefethen, James B. 1975. *An American crusade for wildlife.* Tulsa, Okla.: Boone and Crockett Club and Winchester Press.

U.S. Bureau of Census and U.S. Fish and Wildlife Service. 1980. *National survey of fishing, hunting, and wildlife-associated recreation.* Washington, D.C.: U.S. Government Printing Office.

Yaffee, Steven Lewis. 1983. *Prohibitive policy, implementing the Federal Endangered Species Act.* Cambridge: Massachusetts Institute of Technology Press.

Ziswiler, Vinzenz. 1970. *A biology of extinction and survival.* Rev. English ed., ed. Fred and Pille Bunnell. London: English Universities Press.

Chapter II: What Are Mammals and Where Did They Come From?

Attenborough, David. 1979. *Life on Earth: a natural history.* London: BBC.

Sagan, Carl. 1977. *The dragons of eden: speculations of the evolution of human intelligence.* New York: Random House.

————. 1980. *Cosmos.* New York: Random House.

Wiener, Jonathan. 1983. *The planet Earth.* New York: Bantam.

Wilford, John Noble. 1985. *The riddle of the dinosaur.* New York: Knopf.

Chapter III: Deep Streams: The River Otter

Armstrong, David. 1972. *Distribution of mammals in Colorado.* Monograph of the Museum of Natural History, no. 3. Lawrence: University of Kansas Press.

Cary, Merritt. 1911. *A biological survey of Colorado.* U.S. Department of Agriculture Biological Survey. Washington, D.C.: U.S. Government Printing Office.

Chapman, J. A., and G. A. Feldhammer. 1982. *Wild mammals of North America.* Baltimore: The Johns Hopkins University Press.

Goodman, Patsy. 1984. River otter recovery plan for Colorado. Division of Wildlife nongame wildlife files.

Hoover, J. P. 1984a. Surgical implantation of radiotelemetry devices in American river otters. *Journal of the American Veterinary Medicine Association* 185 (11): 1317–1320.

————. 1984b. Clinical evaluation of American river otters in a reintroduction study. *Journal of the American Veterinary Medicine Association* 185 (11): 1321–1326.

Langlois, D., and J. Sisk. 1980. River otter restoration. Colorado Division of Wildlife Project SE-3-3. Endangered Wildlife Investigation. Division of Wildlife nongame wildlife files.

Lyle, T., and D. Janna. 1979. *Status report on the reintroduced river otter (Lutra canadensis) in the Kawuneeche Valley.* Colorado Division of Wildlife Project SE-3-3. Endangered Wildlife Investigation. Division of Wildlife nongame wildlife files.

Mack, Curtis. 1985. River otter restoration in Grand County, Colorado. M.S. thesis, Colorado State University.

Melquist, W. E. 1981. Ecological aspects of a river otter population in west-central Idaho. Ph.D. diss., University of Idaho.

Robert, M. 1980. Signs of the river otter in the Piedra River. Colorado Division of Wildlife nongame wildlife files.

Seton, Ernest Thompson. 1929. *Lives of game animals.* New York: Doubleday.

Sisk, J. 1984. Signs of the river otter in the Black Canyon of the Gunnison River river otter restoration. Colorado Division of Wildlife Project SE-3-3. Endangered Wildlife Investigations. Colorado Division of Wildlife nongame wildlife files.

Stevens, Dave. 1975. Reintroduction of otter to Rocky Mountain National Park. Special Report. Rocky Mountain National Park. Colorado Division of Wildlife nongame wildlife files.

Warren, Edward Royal. 1942. *The mammals of Colorado, their habits and distribution.* Norman: University of Oklahoma Press.

Wise, M. H. 1980. The use of fish vertebrae in scats for estimating prey size of otters and mink. *Journal of Zoology* 192:25–31.

Chapter IV: Prairie Hills: The Black-Footed Ferret

Adrian, Richard. 1969. The black-footed ferret in South Dakota. South Dakota Department of Game, Fish, and Parks. Photocopy.

Anderson, Maurice. 1978. Black-footed ferret recovery plan. United States Fish and Wildlife Service. Washington, D.C.: U.S. Government Printing Office.

Armstrong, David. 1972. Distribution of mammals in Colorado. Monograph of the Museum of Natural History, no. 3. Lawrence: University of Kansas Press.

Associated Press. 1986. Black forecast on ferrets premature, official warns. *The Denver Post*, February 9.

Cary, Merritt. 1911. *A biological survey of Colorado.* U.S. Department of Agriculture Biological Survey. Washington, D.C.: U.S. Government Printing Office.

Chapman, J. A., and G. A. Feldhammer. 1982. *Wild mammals of North America.* Baltimore: The Johns Hopkins University Press.

Clark, Tim. 1983. *Handbook of methods for locating black-footed ferrets.* Wyoming BLM Wildlife Technical Bulletin no. 2. Bureau of Land Management—Wyoming Division of Game and Fish.

———. 1985. *Black-footed ferret habitat: some management and reintroduction considerations.* Wyoming BLM Wildlife Technical Bulletin no. 2. Bureau of Land Management—Wyoming Division of Game and Fish.

————. 1986. *The black-footed ferret: a monograph*. Great Basin Naturalist Memoir no. 8. Provo: Brigham Young University.

Fagerstone, Kathleen A. 1986. *Summary of black-footed ferret and related research conducted by the Denver Wildlife Research Institute: 1981–1985*. Denver: U.S. Fish and Wildlife Service.

————. In press. *Black-footed ferret, long-tailed weasel, short-tailed weasel, and least weasel*. Denver: U.S. Fish and Wildlife Service.

Frankel, O. H. and M. E. Soule. 1981. *Conservation and evolution*. Cambridge: Cambridge University Press.

Gilbert, Bill. 1980. Missing and presumed to be dead. *Sports Illustrated*, February.

Martin, Stephen, and Max Schroeder. 1982. Search for the black-footed ferret succeeds! *Wyoming Wildlife*, July.

McNulty, Faith. 1970. A reporter at large: the prairie dog and the black-footed ferret. *New Yorker*, June.

Peterson, Iver. 1985. Six endangered ferrets are under strict guard. *Special to the New York Times*, December 15.

Randall, Dick. 1986. Survival crisis at Meeteetse. *Defenders*, January/February.

Richardson, Louise. 1986. On the track of the last black-footed ferrets. *Natural History*, February.

Seton, Ernest Thompson. 1929. *Lives of game animals*. New York: Doubleday.

Warren, Edward Royal. 1942. *The mammals of Colorado, their habits and distribution*. Norman: University of Oklahoma Press.

Weinberg, Dave. 1986. Decline and fall of the black-footed ferret. *Natural History*, February.

United Press International. 1986. State plans aerial search of ferrets. *The Rocky Mountain News*, January 20.

Chapter V: Black Timber: The Wolverine

Armstrong, David. 1972. *Distribution of mammals in Colorado*. Monograph of the Museum of Natural History, no. 3. Lawrence: University of Kansas Press.

Bissell, S. J. 1980. Lynx and wolverine verification report. Colorado Division of Wildlife Project SE-3-3. Endangered Wildlife Investigations. Colorado Division of Wildlife nongame files. Photocopy.

————. 1985. The status of wolverines in Colorado. *Northwest Science* 8, no. 4.

Brown, F. M. 1942. The microscopy of mammalian hairs for the anthropologist. *The Proceedings of the American Philosophical Society* 85:250–274.

Cary, Merritt. 1911. *A biological survey of Colorado*. U.S. Department of Agriculture Biological Survey. Washington, D.C.: U.S. Government Printing Office.

Chapman, J. A., and G. A. Feldhammer. 1982. *Wild mammals of North America*. Baltimore: The Johns Hopkins University Press.

Field, R. J., and G. Feltner. 1974. Wolverine. *Colorado Outdoors* 23:1–6.

Halfpenny, Jim. 1979. Colorado wolverine-lynx verification program. *Journal of the Colorado-Wyoming Academy of Science* 11(1):89.

Hsu, T. C., and K. Benirschke. 1970. *An atlas of mammalian chromosomes.* Vol. 4, folios 151–200. New York: Springer-Verlag.

Mayer, W. V. 1952. The hair of California mammals with keys to the dorsal guard hairs of California mammals. *American Midland Naturalist* 48:480–512.

Newby, F. E., and J. J. McDougal. 1964. Range extension of the wolverine in Montana. *Journal of Mammalogy* 36:485–487.

Seton, Ernest Thompson. 1929. *Lives of game animals.* New York: Doubleday.

Warren, Edward Royal. 1942. *The mammals of Colorado, their habits and distribution.* Norman: University of Oklahoma Press.

Chapter VI: Snow Country: The Lynx

Armstrong, David. 1972. *Distribution of mammals in Colorado.* Monograph of the Museum of Natural History, no. 3. Lawrence: University of Kansas.

Bailey, T. N. 1972. Ecology of bobcats with special reference to social organization. Ph.D. diss., University of Idaho.

Bissell, S. J. 1980. Lynx and wolverine verification report. Colorado Division of Wildlife Project SE-3-3. Endangered Wildlife Investigations. Colorado Division of Wildlife nongame files. Photocopy.

Cary, Merritt. 1911. *A biological survey of Colorado.* U.S. Department of Agriculture Biological Survey. Washington, D.C.: U.S. Government Printing Office.

Chapman, J. A., and G. A. Feldhammer. 1982. *Wild mammals of North America.* Baltimore: The Johns Hopkins University Press.

Denney, R. N. 1975. The status of lynx in Colorado. Report in Colorado Division of Wildlife nongame files. Photocopy.

Gunderson, H. L. 1978. A recent record of a lynx from Nebraska. *Southwestern Naturalist* 23:529.

Halfpenny, Jim. 1979. Colorado wolverine-lynx verification program. *Journal of Colorado-Wyoming Academy of Science* 11(1):89.

Mech, L. David. 1973. Canadian lynx invasion of Minnesota. *Biological Conservation* 5(2):151–152.

————. 1977. Record movement of Canada lynx. *Journal of Mammalogy* 58:676–677.

Nellis, C. H., and S. P. Wetmore. 1969. Long-range movements of lynx in Alberta. *Journal of Mammalogy* 50:640.

Saunder, J. K. 1963. Movements and activities of lynx in Newfoundland. *Journal of Wildlife Management* 27:390–400.

Seton, Ernest Thompson. 1929. *Lives of game animals.* New York: Doubleday.

Terrel, B. 1971. Lynx. *Colorado Outdoors* 20(5):19.

Warren, Edward Royal. 1942. *The mammals of Colorado, their habits and distribution.* Norman: University of Oklahoma Press.

Chapter VII: Side Canyons: The Grizzly Bear

Alt, G., and J. Beecham. 1984. Reintroduction of orphaned black bear cubs into the wild. *Wildlife Society Bulletin* 12:169–174.

Applegate, Roger D. 1979. The germination of cowparsnip seeds from grizzly bear feces. *Journal of Mammalogy* 60(3).

Armstrong, David. 1972. *Distribution of mammals in Colorado*. Monograph of the Museum of Natural History, no. 3. Lawrence: University of Kansas Press.

Associated Press. 1980. Guide who says he slew grizzly with handheld arrow is disputed. *The New York Times*, February 29.

Beck, T., et al. 1982. South San Juan Mountains grizzly bear survey. Colorado Division of Wildlife Project SE-3-4. Endangered Wildlife Investigations. Colorado Division of Wildlife nongame files. Photocopy.

Bissell, S. J. 1980. Grizzly bear incident, September, 1979 summary report. Compendium of reports, maps, photographs, correspondence, and newspaper columns. Colorado Division of Wildlife nongame files.

Brown, David E. 1985. *The grizzly in the Southwest: documentary of an extinction*. Norman: University of Oklahoma Press.

Cary, Merritt. 1911. *A biological survey of Colorado*. U.S. Department of Agriculture Biological Survey. Washington, D.C.: U.S. Government Printing Office.

Chapman, J. A., and G. A. Feldhammer. 1982. *Wild mammals of North America*. Baltimore: The Johns Hopkins University Press.

Christensen, A. C., and M. J. Madel. 1982. Cumulative effects analysis process; grizzly bear habitat component mapping. U.S. Department of Agriculture. Kootenai National Forest.

Clarke, S. H., J. O'Pezio, and C. Hackford. 1980. Fostering black bear cubs in the wild. A paper presented at the International Conference of Bear Research and Management 4:163–166.

Craighead, Frank C. 1979. *Track of the grizzly*. San Francisco: Sierra Club.

Craighead, John J., J. S. Sumner, and G. B. Scaggs. 1982. *A definitive system for analysis of grizzly bear habitat and other wilderness resources*. University of Montana Foundation, Wildlife-Wildlands Monograph.

Craighead, John J., J. Varney, and F. C. Craighead, Jr. 1974. *A population analysis of the Yellowstone grizzly bears*. Montana Forestry Conservation Experimental Station Bulletin no. 40, School of Forestry. Missoula: University of Montana.

Erickson, A. W. 1974. Evaluation of the suitability of the Gila Wilderness for re-establishment of the grizzly bear. Report to the U.S. Forest Service, Southwestern Regional Office, Contract 6-369-74. Typescript.

————. 1978. Grizzly bear management in the Cabinet Mountains of western Montana. United States Forest Service Contract 262-46, Kootenai National Forest. Photocopy.

Gulday, J. C. 1968. Grizzly bears from eastern North America. *American Midlands Naturalist* 79:247–250.

Harris, R. B. 1984. Harvest age structure as an indication of grizzly bear population status. M.S. thesis, University of Montana.

Haynes, B. D., and E. Haynes. 1966. *The grizzly bear: portraits from life*. Norman: University of Oklahoma Press.

Herrero, Stephen. 1985. *Bear attacks: their causes and avoidance*. New York: Nick Lyons.

Jonkel, Charles. 1980. Mexican grizzlies: 1977–1979. Studies; status; habitat recommendations. Border Grizzly Project Final Report 58:1–47. University of Montana.

Jonkel, Charles, Peter Husby, Richard Russell, and John Beecham. 1977. The reintroduction of orphaned grizzly bear cubs into the wild. In *Bears — their biology and management*. A selection of papers from the 4th International Conference on Bear Research and Management. Washington, D.C.: Bear Biology Association and U.S. Government Printing Office.

Kistchinski, A. A. 1970. Life history of the brown bear (*Ursus arctos linnaeus*) in northeast Siberia. In *Bears — their biology and management*. A selection of papers from the 2nd International Conference on Bear Research and Management. Morges, Switzerland: International Union for Conservation of Nature and Natural Resources.

Knight, Richard R., et al. 1975–1986. *Yellowstone grizzly bear investigations: annual reports of the interagency study team*.

Koford, C. B. 1969. *The last of the Mexican grizzly bear*. Morges, Switzerland: International Union for Conservation of Nature and Natural Resources Bulletin 95.

Leopold, A. Starker. 1958. Situacion del oso plateado in Chihuahua. *Review of the Society of Mexican Natural History* 19:115–120.

———. 1967. Grizzlies of the Sierra del Nido. *Pacific Discovery* 20:30–32.

———. 1972. *Wildlife of Mexico*. Berkeley: University of California Press.

Mace, R., and M. Haroldson. 1984. Scope of work and proposed study design: grizzly bear population augmentation. Report to U.S. Fish and Wildlife Service. Grizzly Bear Recovery Coordinator. Photocopy.

Mysterud, Ivar. 1977. Bear management and sheep husbandry in Norway, with a discussion of predatory behavior significant for evaluation of livestock losses. In *Bears — their biology and management*. A selection of papers from the 4th International Conference on Bear Research and Management. Washington, D.C.: Bear Biology Association and U.S. Government Printing Office.

Murray, John A. 1985. A last look at the grizzly, the story of a two year search for grizzly bears in Colorado. *Colorado Outdoors* 34(6):28–33.

Nelson, Ralph A., et al. 1977. Behavior, biochemistry, and hibernation in black, grizzly, and polar bears. In *Bears — their biology and management*. A selection of papers from the 4th International Conference on Bear Research and Management. Washington, D.C.: Bear Biology Association and U.S. Government Printing Office.

Pearson, A. M. 1975. *The northern interior grizzly bear, Ursus arctos linnaeus*. Canadian Wildlife Service report series no. 34. University of Alberta.

Roop, Larry J. 1976–1986. Grizzly bear progress report. Wyoming Game and

Fish Department. Photocopy.

Roosevelt, Theodore. 1983. *American bears*. Ed. Paul Schullery. Boulder: Colorado Associated University Press.

Russell, Andy. 1967. *Grizzly country*. New York: Knopf.

Scaggs, G. B. 1979. Vegetation description of potential grizzly bear habitat in the Selway-Bitterroot area, Montana and Idaho. M.S. thesis, University of Montana.

Schneider, Bill. 1977a. *Where the grizzly walks*. Missoula: Mountain Press.

———. 1977b. Will this grizzly attack? *National Wildlife*, February/March.

———. 1978. Last fight for the grizzly. *Outdoor Life*, January.

Schullery, Paul. 1980. *The bears of Yellowstone*. Yellowstone Park, Wyo.: Yellowstone Library and Museum Association.

Servheen, Christopher. 1981. Denning ecology, food habits, habitat use, and movements of grizzly bears in the Mission Mountains, Montana. Ph.D. diss., University of Montana.

———. In press. *The management of the threatened grizzly bear in the conterminous United States*. Grizzly Bear Recovery Coordinator.

Servheen, Christopher, W. Kaworm, and A. Christensen. In press. Grizzly bear population augmentation in the Cabinet Mountains, Montana. Paper presented to 7th International Conference on Bear Research and Management. Grizzly Bear Recovery Coordinator.

Seton, Ernest Thompson. 1899. *The biography of a grizzly*. New York: Grosset and Dunlap.

———. 1929. *Lives of game animals*. New York: Doubleday.

Shaffer, Mark L. 1978. Determining minimum viable population sizes: a case study of the grizzly bear. Ph.D. diss., Duke University.

Shaffer, Mark L., and F. Samson. 1985. Population size and extinction: a note on determining critical population sizes. *American Naturalist* 125:144–152.

Storer, Tracy I., and Lloyd P. Tevis, Jr. 1955. *California grizzly*. Lincoln: University of Nebraska Press.

Suchy, W. J., L. L. McDonald, M. D. Strickland, and S. H. Anderson. 1985. New estimates of minimum viable population size for grizzly bears of the Yellowstone ecosystem. *Wildlife Society Bulletin:* 223–228.

Trevino, J. C., and Charles Jonkel. 1983. Do grizzlies still live in Mexico? Paper presented to the 6th International Conference on Bear Research and Management.

United States Department of Agriculture, Forest Service, and United States Department of the Interior, National Park Service. 1979. *Guidelines for management involving grizzly bears in the greater Yellowstone area*.

United States Department of the Interior, Fish and Wildlife Service, Office of Endangered Species. 1982. *Grizzly bear recovery plan*.

Warren, Edward Royal. 1942. *The mammals of Colorado, their habits and distribution*. Norman: University of Oklahoma Press.

Wright, William H. [1909] 1977. *The grizzly bear.* Reprint. Lincoln: University of Nebraska Press.

Young, F. M., and C. Beyers. 1980. *Man meets grizzly.* Boston: Houghton Mifflin.

Zunino, F. 1981. Dilemma of the Abruzzo bears. *Oryx* 16(2):153–156.

Chapter VIII: Winter Range: The Gray Wolf

Allen, Durward. 1979. *The wolves of Minong.* Boston: Houghton Mifflin.

Armstrong, David. 1972. *Distribution of mammals in Colorado.* Monograph of the Museum of Natural History, no. 3. Lawrence: University of Kansas.

Bjorge, R. R. 1980. Management and research of the wolf-livestock conflict in Alberta. In *Proceedings of the Canadian Pest Management Society.* Edmonton.

Boyd, Diane. 1982. Food habits and spatial relations of coyotes and a lone wolf in the Rocky Mountains. M.S. thesis, University of Montana.

Brown, David E. 1982. *The wolf in the Southwest.* Tucson: University of Arizona Press.

Carbyn, L. N. 1980. *Ecology and management of wolves in Riding Mountain National Park, Manitoba.* Canadian Wildlife Service Report no. 10. University of Alberta.

Cary, Merritt. 1911. *A biological survey of Colorado.* U.S. Department of Agriculture Biological Survey. Washington, D.C.: U.S. Government Printing Office.

Chapman, J. A., and G. A. Feldhammer. 1982. *Wild mammals of North America.* Baltimore: The Johns Hopkins University Press.

Conley, Herbert, Jr. 1976. Impacts of reintroducing gray wolves into the Rocky Mountain National Park area. M.S. thesis, Colorado State University.

Cowan, I. M. 1947. The timber wolf in the Rocky Mountain National Parks of Canada. *Canadian Journal of Research* 25:139–174.

Dawinks, R. 1976. *The selfish gene.* Oxford: Oxford University Press.

De La Funete, F. R. 1975. Protection of the wolf in Spain—notes on a public awareness campaign. In *Wolves,* ed. D. H. Pimlott, 103–112. IUCN Publication Services, Supplementary Paper no. 43, Morges, Switzerland.

Fritts, S. H. 1982. *Wolf depredation on livestock in Minnesota.* USDI Fish and Wildlife Service Resource Publication 145. Washington, D.C.: U.S. Government Printing Office.

Fuller, W. A. 1966. *The biology and management of the bison of Wood Buffalo National Park.* Canadian Wildlife Service Report. Management Bulletin Series 1 (11). University of Alberta.

Fuller, W. A., and L. B. Keith. 1980. Wolf population dynamics and prey relationships in northeastern Alberta. *Journal of Wildlife Management* 44:583–602.

Garzon, I. 1974. Especies en peligro—el lobo. *Adrena* no. 8, WWF.

Greek Ministry of National Economy. 1975. The kill of wolves in Greece,

1964–1972. In *Wolves*, ed. D. H. Pimlott, 81–82. IUCN Publication Services, Supplementary Paper no. 43, Morges, Switzerland.

Gunson, J. R. 1983. Wolf predation of livestock in western Canada. Paper in *Wolves in Canada and Alaska: their status, biology, and management*, ed. L. N. Carbyn. Canadian Wildlife Service Report no. 45.

Gunson, J. R., and R. R. Bjorge. 1983. Wolf predation of cattle on the Simonette River pastures in northwestern Alberta. In *Wolves in Canada and Alaska: their status, biology, and management*, ed. L. N. Carbyn. Canadian Wildlife Service Report no. 45.

Haber, G. 1977. The socio-ecological dynamics of wolves and prey in a subarctic ecosystem. Ph.D. diss., University of British Columbia.

Lopez, Barry. 1984. *Of wolves and men*. New York: Knopf.

Lorenz, Konrad. 1963. *Das sogenannte böse*. Wien: Dr. G. Borotha-Schoeler Verlag.

McNamee, Tom. 1986. Yellowstone's missing element. *Audubon*, January.

Mech, L. David. 1970. *The wolf—the ecology and behavior of an endangered species*. New York: Doubleday.

———. 1977a. Productivity, mortality, and population trend of wolves in northeastern Minnesota. *Journal of Mammalogy* 58:559–574.

———. 1977b. Wolf pack buffer zones as prey reservoirs. *Science* 198:320–321.

———. 1978. The wolf: an introduction to its behavior, ecology, and conservation. Paper presented to the International Wolf Symposium, April, at Edinburgh, Scotland.

Mowat, Farley. 1965. *Never cry wolf*. New York: Dell.

Murie, Adolph. 1944. *The wolves of Mt. McKinley*. U.S. National Park Service, Fauna Series 5. Washington, D.C.: U.S. Government Printing Office (reprinted in 1982 by The University of Washington Press, Seattle).

Murray, John. 1987. The wolf in Colorado: past and future. *Colorado Outdoors*, March/April.

Myberget, S. 1978. The past and present of the wolf in Norway. Paper presented at the International Wolf Symposium, April, at Edinburgh, Scotland.

Peterson, Rolf. 1974. Wolf ecology and prey relationship on Isle Royale. Ph.D. diss., Purdue University.

Pulliainen, E. 1978. The present status of the wolf in Finland and adjacent areas. Paper presented at the International Wolf Symposium, April, at Edinburgh, Scotland.

Rumanian Academy, Natural Monuments Committee. 1975. Data of the situation of the wolf in Rumania. In *Wolves*, ed. D. H. Pimlott, 44–52. IUCN Publication Services, Supplementary Paper no. 43, Morges, Switzerland.

Seton, Ernest Thompson. 1929. *Lives of game animals*. New York: Doubleday.

Slovak Institute for the Conservation of Natural Monuments. 1975. Status, distribution, and problems of protecting wolves in Slovakia. In *Wolves*, ed. D. H.

Pimlott, 63–72. IUCN Publication Services, Supplementary Paper no. 43, Morges, Switzerland.

Suminski, P. 1978. *The wolf in Poland.* Paper presented at the International Wolf Symposium, April, at Edinburgh, Scotland.

Tompa, F. S. 1981. Problem wolf management in British Columbia: conflict and program evaluation. In *Proceedings* of the IUCN Wolf Workshop, Edmonton, Alberta.

United States Department of the Interior, Fish and Wildlife Service, Office of Endangered Species. 1982. *Northern Rocky Mountain timber wolf recovery plan,* rev. 1986. U.S. Government Printing Office.

Weaver, J. 1981. Wolf-livestock relationships: a profile and perspective. United States Forest Service. Unpublished. Photocopy.

Weise, T. F. 1975. An experimental translocation of the eastern timber wolf. *Audubon Conservation Report* 5:1–28.

Warren, Edward Royal. 1942. *The mammals of Colorado, their habits and distribution.* Norman: University of Oklahoma Press.

Zimen, Eric. 1976a. Das wolfsgeschehen im bayerischen wald. *National-Park* 3(76):5–10.

————. 1976b. Wolf reintroduction: suitable areas and techniques. In *Reintroductions: techniques and ethics,* ed. L. Boitani, 151–161, Serie Atti e Studi no. 2, WWF, Rome.

————. 1978. *Der wolf: mythos und verhalten* (translated in 1981 by Delacorte Press, New York). Munchen: Meyster Verlag.

Zimen, Eric, and L. Boitani. 1975. Number and distribution of the wolf in Italy. *Zeitschrift für Säugetierkunde* 40:102–112.

————. 1978. Status of the wolf in Europe and possibilities of conservation and reintroduction. In *The behavior and ecology of wolves.* New York: Garland Press.

Chapter IX: The Years to Come

Abbey, Edward. 1984. *Beyond the wall, essays from the outside.* New York: Holt, Rinehart, and Winston.

Halfpenny, Jim. 1986. *A field guide to mammal tracking in western America.* Boulder: Johnson.

Ehrlich, Gretel. 1985. *The solace of open spaces.* New York: Viking.

Garreau, Joel. 1981. *The nine nations of North America.* Boston: Houghton Mifflin.

Hart, Richard E., ed. 1980. *The future of agriculture in the Rocky Mountains.* Salt Lake City: Westwater Press.

Jonas, Frank H. 1969. *Politics in the American West.* Salt Lake City: University of Utah Press.

Lamm, Richard D., and Michael McCarthy. 1982. *The angry West, a vulnerable land and its future*. Boston: Houghton Mifflin.

Lavender, David. [1943] 1977. *One man's West*. Lincoln: University of Nebraska Press.

Nash, Gerald D. 1973. *The American West in the twentieth century*. Englewood Cliffs, N.J.: Prentice-Hall.

Raven, Peter. 1986. The urgency of tropical conservation. *The Nature Conservancy News*, January-March.

Schultheis, Rob. 1983. *The hidden West, journeys in the American outback*. San Francisco: North Point Press.

United States of America Civil Code. 1983. *The Endangered Species Act as amended by public law 97–304* (The Endangered Species Act Amendments of 1982). Washington, D.C.: U.S. Government Printing Office.

Index